The Valley
of
The Butterflies

Memoirs of the French Midi

About the Author

Peter Kinsley is an Anglo-Irish novelist, born in Avoca House in Stanley, Co. Durham. He was educated at St Cuthbert's grammar school, Benwell, Northumberland. After service in the British Army with Allied Land Forces, Central Europe (ALFCE) in Fontainbleau, France, 1953-55, he was a sub-editor on the *Daily Mirror*, Fleet Street, aged 21. Later he was a crime reporter on the *Daily Mail* and the *Daily Express*, and wrote the William Hickey column before resigning, aged 26, to freelance as a foreign correspondent in the south of France and Rome for the BBC and fourteen British newspapers, and met many of the famous people and the extraordinary characters he portrays in his four volumes of memoirs, set in Newcastle, Manchester, London, Paris, Rome, Istanbul and the Greek Islands, Cyprus, Israel, The French Riviera, Germany, Austria, Jugoslavia, Bulgaria, Romania, sailing the Spanish coast and islands with Tristan Jones, New York, Minneapolis, and Mexico, and, last but not least, Ibiza.

NOTE: The author thanks the Society of Authors and the Royal Literary Fund, for their generous help, enabling him to complete these volumes of memoirs.

The Valley
of
The Butterflies

Peter Kinsley

AMHERST

A CIP catalogue record for this book is available
from the British Library.

ISBN 1 903637 07 4

Printed in Great Britain

First published in 2002 by

Amherst Publishing Limited
Longmore House, High Street, Otford, Sevenoaks, Kent TN14 5PQ

I, on my side, require of every writer,
first or last, a simple and sincere
account of his own life, and not merely
what he has heard of other men's lives.

- Henry David Thoreau (1817 - 1862)

By the same author

COMEDY:
Three Cheers For Nothing

THRILLERS:
Pimpernel 60
The Vatchman Switch
The Pistolero

INVESTIGATION:
I'm Jack - The Police Hunt for the Yorkshire Ripper

MEMOIRS:
Volume I
All the Fields Are Covered With Snow (1934 - 1948)
Volume II
Don't Tell My Mother I'm A Newspaperman (1950 - 1963)
Volume III
Bogged Down In County Lyric (1964 - 1984)
Volume IV
The Valley of The Butterflies (1980 - 1990)

What they said about Volume I

Loved the book — it made me laugh and cry. — **Neal Ascherson**, (author of *The King Incorporated* and a columnist on *The Observer*).

A lovingly detailed record of a World War II childhood and a threadbare, innocent world that is now as lost as Ur of the Chaldees - **Al Alvarez** (author of *The Savage God*, formerly the poetry editor of *The Observer*).

A fascinating record of young lives in the Second World War - **Penny Ritchie Calder**, Curator, Imperial War Museum, London.

A wartime story that took forty years to tell... now to be used in a major exhibition 'Children At War' at the Imperial War Museum, London - **Matthew McKenzie**, *Sunday Sun*, Newcastle Upon Tyne.

What they said about Volume II

This is the most vivid and entertaining account written of the 'Last Age' of Fleet Street - the era when the basic irreverence and humanity of journalists finally broke through into the pages of their own newspapers. Peter Kinsley, who worked on papers in northern England and as a self employed British correspondent on the French Riviera, belonged to the great period of the tabloid and popular 'diaries': the gossip columns which ostensibly chronicled the high life of the Establishment, but which did so with an increasingly radical ferocity that discredited and punctured the high-and-mighty. Nobody reading Kinsley will go on believing that the 1950s were a dull decade The procession of laughing , outrageous reprobates in his pages (some journalists, some their victims)shows very clearly how the way was being opened for the 'Satire Boom' of London in the 1960s. These two books of memoir are a wonderfully comic read but they are also infallible source material for anyone studying the 'end of deference' in Britain and the prelude to the head-on political and social challenges in the next period - **Neal Ascherson.**

A nostalgic walk down memory lane for those who recall the halcyon days of Fleet Street. Peter recounts with humour many stories concerning himself and the Greats who bestrode the Street in those times. He also reminds us of what great fun it could be, an element that seems sadly missing in today's newspaper world

This is the second part of four volumes. The first, All The Fields Are Covered with Snow, is a lyrical and deeply moving account of his wartime evacuation to a depressed coalmining village, incongruously named No Place - **Alfred Draper**, (author of The Amritsar Massacre)..

What they said about Volume III

Bogged Down in County Lyric forms the third volume of a projected quartet, the narrative being taken up where the author left off in Volume Two, *Don't Tell My Mother I'm a Newspaperman...*

Kinsley, who styles himself 'McGinn' and writes in the third person throughout, arrives in New York on the eve of the American launch of his first novel, *Three Cheers for Nothing.* We follow some breathless globe-hopping for eleven chapters before eventually coming to rest in Ibiza's Calle Mayor. The year is 1969, inland from Murcia people are just coming to grips with forks, and off the Ibizan waterfront, Seley [Steve Primero] is expounding the principal advantage of life on the White Island: 'You can get a litre of gin for nothing. Of course, you have to eat the occasional orange for your health.'

George Llewellyn was master of ceremonies at the George & Dragon, a bar in the Calle Mayor, nearby Wauna's being owned by a large and formidable Anglo-American (Wauna Paul) who played up the fire-breathing beast for passing trade. Many of the best one-liners come from this amazing duo, and the present writer [Martin Davies] takes off his hat to Peter Kinsley for having the presence of mind and journalistic savvy to record them for posterity.

It is quite a line-up: Steve Primero, the archetypal alcoholic writer, penniless, perennially plastered, quick to take offence and unrelentingly rude; Tristan Jones, an old salt with a wicked sense of humour; George and Wauna with their rapier-like repartee; Doreen on her perch in the corner ('I'm half Irish and half pissed and I came to Spain to get away from twats like you.')...

The reviewer is spoiled by the sheer number of anecdotes in this marvellous book.

- Martin Davies, Bibliomaniacs' Corner on www.liveibiza.com

CHAPTER 1

PETER McGinn was always reminded that he was living in the French Midi when Pierre the farmer and wine-grower paid for his round of drinks with a dead pigeon. Sometimes he paid with a dozen eggs (funny how the French do everything in tens until it comes to eggs when they use dozens and half dozens) and sometimes with tomatoes or a rabbit - but this time it was a pigeon. He took it, nonchalantly, out of the voluminous pocket of the faded corduroy jacket he wore every day except Sunday, and placed it on the bar counter. McGinn knew he had another in his 'poacher's pocket', but that was in reserve for the next bar. He had mentally totted up the price of the drinks we had consumed until the bill reached the current market price of a pigeon, and then flopped it on the counter for the *patron* to inspect its plumpness. This was not your ordinary common or garden pigeon seen on display at a butcher's shop, but a home-raised, corn-fed, fat champion of a pigeon whose flesh contained secret ingredients to make the bar owner and his wife sigh over its delicious flavour.

It was accepted and the *patron* bought a last round of drinks before they moved on.

At the farm on Sunday, where he had been invited to join the family at lunch, Peter McGinn was to learn the secret ingredients when Siddo, Pierre's wife, was complimented on the flavour of the chicken she had just served.

'Wild thyme and rosemary,' she said. 'I mix the wild herbs, which come from the hills above Cabrière, in with the chicken and pigeon feed and that flavours the flesh.'

'It's the best chicken I've ever tasted,' McGinn said, and she smiled. Siddo, which was diminutive of her full name Sidonie, loved a compliment, especially about her cooking. McGinn had watched a few days earlier when she had hung the chicken by its trussed feet from a branch of the walnut tree that grew in the farmyard and expertly slit its throat with a quarter-moon knife blade, then plunged the carcase into a black cauldron of boiling water, kept there for just that purpose, and swiftly pluck the feathers into a hole in the ground.

Siddo had noticed him watching her, and he could see what she was thinking: that the look indicated to her that he thought her a little bit savage the way she had callously and indifferently killed the chicken.

'When you are a farmer's wife, you have to do these things,' she said.

'Of course.'

'One must eat, after all,' she added, smiling at the foreigner's squeamishness as the chicken feathers, caught by a light breeze, fluttered around in the farmyard, and the big, fawn and white guard dog, Lekka, began to howl in anticipation of the remains that would come its way later.

Peter McGinn considered himself fortunate to be invited to eat every Sunday with a French farmer and his family, a privilege rarely extended to foreigners in France.

Looking around Siddo's kitchen, he could see that this was the most important room in the farmhouse: there was a family-size food blender, a Moulinex coffee-bean grinder, a head-high refrigerator with freezer compartment, a machine for making ice-cream, and one for making yoghurt, and a chest-freezer in an annexe of the kitchen containing garden produce and the frozen carcasses of rabbits and ducks. There was a dish-washer and a large gas cooker, the top covered with silver foil around the burners to catch the drips and save cleaning. Finally there was a micro-wave oven for warming the stuffed tomatoes, aubergines and courgettes which she prepared when the vegetables were in season and put down in the chest freezer for winter days when the garden was empty and the land bare.

That spring, McGinn had rented an apartment, which in fact turned out to be a whole house with two wine cellars, in the 14th century Ghetto of Pézenas, from Siddo, whose family owned the building in the Rue des d'André, and as he often bumped into her husband, Pierre, in one of the bars during *apéritif* hour 7-8 p.m., the Sunday lunch became a standing invitation, McGinn's contribution being a box of cakes for the children.

It was on the third Sunday that he asked where the toilet was.

'Oh - just go in the vines,' said Pierre.

'Well, no - is there a toilet with a seat?'

He had never been upstairs in the farmhouse, where there were six bedrooms, their windows overlooking the farmyard, and he assumed that there would be a bathroom and toilet there, and by indicating the vines Pierre was simply saving McGinn a journey.

They looked slightly embarrassed.

'If you go past the chicken houses on the edge of the vineyard, you'll see a shed,' said Pierre.

Lekka the guard dog cast a baleful eye at McGinn as he walked through the yard. The dog was becoming accustomed to him but McGinn gave him a wide berth nevertheless and he knew the length of his chain.

There it stood, in all its glory, a battered privy made out of old planks with so many gaps between them it could have served as a watch-tower with views on all sides. It stood over a hole in the ground, and the seat was made from a railway sleeper which looked as if it had served its time when Isambard Kingdom Brunel was a boy apprentice. It was what used to be called a midden in Scotland and the North of England in the thirties and forties until local councils replaced them with flush lavatories.

It was a sure indicator of French priorities: a dish-washer, a micro-wave oven, a deep freeze, food blender and every modern machine and convenience for producing every kind of dish in the kitchen - but no toilet!

Back in the farmhouse, McGinn said: 'I've never seen an antique toilet before,' and Pierre and Siddo laughed. 'But what happens later?'

'I dig another hole and move the shed,' said Pierre.

'Dominique,' said Siddo, addressing her eldest daughter, 'There's some salad left over for Pony - will you go and fetch him?'

Dominique went out of the dining room and through the kitchen and around to the stable, returning a few minutes later leading a stout little pony by its mane. The animal certainly knew its way, picking its hooves carefully down the steps and advancing on the dining table to be fed lettuce leaves by Siddo.

'What's its name?' McGinn asked.

'Pony. That's its name,' said Siddo.

'He's getting old now,' said Dominique, 'but he used to take us to church on Sunday mornings in the cart.'

With that they all trooped out to the stable to view the splendid little wooden cart which, with Siddo at the reins, was demonstrated in the farmyard, with the three children aboard, cheering her on.

What McGinn realised about this farmer and his wife was that they were trying to be as self-sufficient as it was possible to be in a modern world. The Sunday lunch always ran to five or six courses, starting with eggs mayonnaise and tomatoes, peas with chopped ham or asparagus, chicken, duck or pigeon from the farm, and salad from the garden, then cheese. The fruit trees provided fruit tarts, and the walnut tree provided the basis for *vin noix* - nut wine - an *apéritif* full of flavour. Pierre used the barter system, with his eggs, rabbits, chickens, ducks and pigeons, to buy other items, to pay garage bills and the odd bar bill, and, in season, sold his tomatoes, onions, aubergines, courgettes, peppers, to local buyers. Their cash necessities were petrol, oil, bottled gas, flour, rice, olive oil and cooking oil, sugar, coffee, milk, bread, the electricity bill, and clothing for the family.

The French have always been a conservative and practical people. During the Second World War they used wood-burning stoves on the back of cars to make them run, and during a fuel shortage in France that year, Pierre and other *vignerons* used mazout oil (normally heating fuel) in their cars and restricted the speed to 30 kilometres an hour so as not to damage the engines. The family car was rarely used for shopping. Siddo sped off on her moped and whizzed around the bakers' shops and grocers in the town three times a week.

Siddo had been on her moped when she caught McGinn up on his way to the farm. 'Are you the Englishman looking for an apartment? Were you at the Syndicate d'Initiative just now?'

Another lesson he was to learn in the Midi - news travels fast. No sooner had he left the Syndicate office but the girl had telephoned Siddo about a possible tenant.

First they went to the farm to meet Pierre and drink a customary glass of wine. It was not done to rush into any business arrangements in the Midi. Sometimes a stranger would be invited twice or even three times to discuss buying something, meeting other interested members of the family, especially if it involved the sale of a family-owned property. With the formalities of introduction to Pierre completed, they went to view the apartment in the Rue des d'André which ran parallel to the Rue des Juiverie, both streets about wide enough to push a hand-cart and the whole area overflowing with cats of all colours, shapes and sizes. Freda White had called Pézenas the 'town of cats' in her book on the Languedoc, and the cat population only began to diminish when the Town Hall distributed green plastic sacks of rat poison and the swarm of cats became unnecessary.

Freda White also said the local men were in the daily habit of drinking about three litres of the local 'pinard', which is their word for 10 or 11 degree table wine. Although some of the locals think the word derives from the pine barrels on long boats on the *Canal du Midi*, used to transport wine in the old days, it actually comes from the grape called 'pinot'.

A house-painter was at work, completing the window sill when we arrived, the finishing touch to the newly-painted apartment which turned out to be only part of the whole building of two wine cellars, the second floor flat and on the third floor an enormous attic in the eaves which would have made a good studio for a painter.

So when McGinn broached the subject of wine-drinking in the Herault region of Languedoc, Siddo pretended to be taken aback: 'Three litres a day? Oh, no. Absolutely not true. A glass or two with lunch and a glass or two with dinner, perhaps, but three litres a day? That's impossible.'

She looked to the painter for confirmation. He laughed the whole idea off immediately. 'These stories,' he said, 'amazing. They invent them up North to make us look like a bunch of alcoholics down here. The people are so cold up there, they try to associate our natural warmth with drinking.' He laughed again. 'Three litres? Absolute nonsense.'

He went on painting, leaning through the open window. It was a few minutes to midday and McGinn knew that he would be edging to go for his lunch at exactly twelve when the clock struck in the church tower, the habit of a lifetime.

McGinn would come to know that particular time of the day in the months to come, for it was only between twelve and one o'clock that the sun reached down to touch that window sill. For the rest of the time, the Ghetto was in shadow.

There was a sudden shout on the stairs: *'Monsieur Maurice. Monsieur Maurice. Vous êtes la?'*

The painter put his brush on the sill. *'Oui,'* he shouted at the open door, and Siddo went to see who was calling. A woman of about 70 years of age was painfully climbing the stairs. 'Oh Monsieur Maurice, I'm glad I've found you,' she cried, 'You must come and help me.'

'What's the problem, Madam Lelu?' the painter asked.

'It's my lodger. He's making trouble again. You have to come and help me, Monsieur Maurice. I cannot control him. He's breaking cups and using foul language.'

'That's terrible, Madame Lelu,' said Siddo, sympathetic, 'Do you want me to come too?'

'No, Monsieur Maurice has helped me before. He knows how to handle him. You see the problem is that he is drinking three litres of wine every day, like most of his friends...'

Siddo looked at McGinn and then at the painter. The painter looked at McGinn and then at Siddo. The clock struck twelve. He put his brush in white spirit. The job was done. He put his coat on, packed his things and moved towards the door, still looking thoughtful and glancing again at Siddo.

'Touché, Monsieur,' he said to McGinn out of the side of his mouth, as he made his exit in the wake of Madame Lelu.

Pierre and Siddo often laughed about it later at the farm during their Sunday lunches, as Pierre urged McGinn on to take another glass of red wine. Once McGinn asked him what happened to all the white wine and rosé wine that was made in the region. There was plenty of it because when he had visited the Co-operative and laughed at that little brass kitchen tap protruding from what looked like a small church filled with millions of gallons and the word *'rouge'* in chalk above the tap, there were two similar vats alongside marked *'rosé'* and *'blanc'* - or what amounted to a veritable cathedral of wine.

'They keep it for the women and children,' Pierre replied, 'and for christenings and first communions.'

Pierre always looked at the first course of eggs and tomatoes with the kind of loathing an American child reserves for breakfast cereal - something he is forced to eat. Pierre was a meat man. The salad he would suffer for his health, but his eyes would light up at the sight of the main dish and also at the sight of the cheese board which always had a big portion of Roquefort which he ate mixed with half-salted butter as many French people do, for the flavour is so strong.

The people in this region were very proud of the Roquefort from St. Affrique in the Aveyron, without any doubt the world's greatest cheese, and tasting it on Sunday gave McGinn the opportunity of telling Pierre and Siddo about a cheese made in the Pyrenees which is matured in cows' urine. They both made a face and he doubted if they believed it, but then he told them about a family in Corsica who stored their cheese in caves but the snails started to eat the cheese. Being French and practical, they ate the snails and discovered they had acquired a delicious flavour from their cheese, and from then on specially put aside some cheese for the snails to eat. That they believed wholeheartedly and said they would have done the same. Then Pierre capped the snail stories with one of his own - on how he proved his manhood to his future father-in-law, Siddo's Dad, by eating snails...

'I was nervous meeting him for the first time, as he was a high-ranking Gendarme with a reputation for toughness acquired in French-occupied Germany after the war. When we shook hands he looked very hard at me and said: "Do you like snails?" "Of course I do, Monsieur. Am I not French?" I replied.

'"How many do you eat?" he persisted.

'"Fifty", I boasted, because I knew he was testing me.

'"I always eat a hundred," he said. "When do we start?"

'I realised he was challenging me to a snail-eating contest. I was being forced to prove myself and my manhood as a Frenchman before he would consent to give his daughter's hand in marriage.

'We met at his house. He was in uniform, silver epaulettes, medals, ribbons, the lot. There was no sign of his wife or of Siddo. This was to be a men-only affair. He had cooked two hundred snails. They were to be eaten cold, with mayonnaise.

'He produced this enormous aluminium pot with 200 snails in it and began to share them out, twenty-five onto each plate, counting them carefully as he did so. Then he bade me help myself to mayonnaise.

'"Good?" he asked, after the first plateful.

'"Excellent" I said, and we discussed my Army service in Algeria and his service in Germany and Beziers rugby team's chances of being champions of France once again.

'When he shovelled out that final plateful of twenty-five snails he knew that I was flagging and he looked very hard at me, as if to say: if you don't eat them all, you will remain a bachelor for the rest of your life.

'The things you do for love,' Pierre sighed at the memory. 'I imagined myself in the Tour de France with just one more mountain to climb or twenty-five kilometres to race and I would be King of the Mountains, win the *maillot jaune*, the yellow jersey, and be famous. So I staggered on and finished the last plateful and thought that I would never need to or want to eat again as long as I lived, like after a Christmas lunch.

'"Cheese?" he said, producing a cheese board which had at least twenty-five maturing goat cheeses on it.

'"I always round off a good meal with a little goat cheese," he said.

'I cut a tiny triangle out of one of them and nibbled it, looking expectantly at him.

'"Welcome to the family," he said.'

Siddo clapped her hands with delight at this oft-repeated story of Pierre's, and went to fetch the cakes for the children who had clearly heard it all before, but had politely sat through it without fidgeting.

In the coming months McGinn was to learn many things about these wine growers of Languedoc and their way of life. A farmer would not have dreamed of offering to help his wife in the kitchen, nor would his sons. Pierre never offered and Siddo would no more have allowed him to cook or wash up than she would have attempted to drive the tractor or prune the vines. There was a division of labour that had existed for centuries, and it left the menfolk helpless when they had to fend for themselves. A farmer whose wife died would not consider it in bad taste to advertise for a new wife or to seek help from a matrimonial agency, for his mother and then his wife or sisters had cared for him all his life.

When Siddo and the children went on holiday - a rare event for a

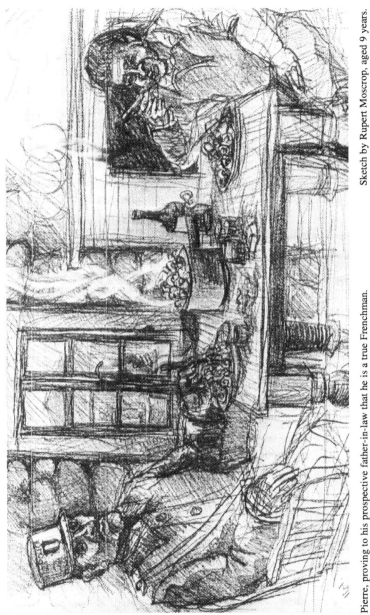

Sketch by Rupert Moscrop, aged 9 years.

Pierre, proving to his prospective father-in-law that he is a true Frenchman.

farmer's wife, but she was combining it with selling a piece of land -
McGinn called on Pierre to see how he was managing and found that
Siddo had cooked ten days' meals in advance for him and all he had to
do was take them from the refrigerator and warm them in the oven.
McGinn was surprised she hadn't left instructions for him on how to
light the oven.

Another time, when Pierre opened the refrigerator door, there were
thirty melons with a slice out of each one. When he asked him about
this he said: 'I try each melon. If it is not perfect, I feed it to the animals.'

In a bar, no matter how good the conversation or the comradeship,
at ten minutes to eight the farmers would be looking at the time and
thinking of *'souper.'* The cafés would empty as if by magic. If anyone
(any foreigner) had had the temerity to suggest that, instead of going
home they had a couple of extra drinks, played another game of cards
and went home late, just for a change, they would look shocked and
say: 'Why? I must eat my supper.'

The grape farmers may well have been masters of their vines and
their tractors, but their wives ruled the household, and heaven help any
one of them who turned up late for *'souper'* - which meant that they
had continued drinking. The wives also controlled the purse strings,
and most of them resented every franc handed across a bar. They
themselves did not drink and rarely entered a café or bar, except perhaps
for a wedding feast or christening or first communion celebration. If
asked if they drank, the reply, invariably, was: *'Que de l'eau.'* 'Only
water,' for alcohol to most French women is poison: it is fattening, it
ruins the figure, bloats the face and causes wrinkles, and if the men
wanted to indulge, well, that was their affair, just so long as it didn't eat
into the family finances.

McGinn was to discover that most *vignerons* or *viticulteurs* tippled
in their *caves*. There was always a ready supply in vats and barrels, and
a length of rubber tube and a few old glasses lying about... Looking
through the open door of a *cave* and seeing a farmer sharpening a scythe
just before the hour of the apéritif, midday or evening, one noticed that
he was sharpening it just a little too slowly and carefully and had a
rather glazed look about the eyes.

Eventually the doctor would call a halt to all this tippling and the
farmer would realise with a start that his liver and kidneys were not

made of reinforced concrete like the vats that contain his wine, and he would be forced to join the wifely chorus of *'Que de l'eau'*. A wave of sympathy could be felt in the bar when a gnarled and wizened old farmer who had heard the doctor's dreaded sentence after a lifetime of tasting the miraculous nectars he produced on his farm, approach the counter, and, with a voice that sounded like a mixture of a rusty sledge being dragged over sandpaper and a Speak-Your-Weight machine saying: 'Smoking is a health hazard', order his new drink: *'Vichy menthe'* or water with mint flavour, pronounced *Vichy mant* with Midi accent.

The Sunday lunches usually ended around about four in the afternoon with a sing-song, the children giving a squeaky rendering of *'Frere Jacques'* or *'Sous le pont d'Avignon'*, and Pierre singing 'Ma Normandie', and Siddo putting military marching songs on the record player and singing along with them, and a contribution from McGinn in the form of a Georges Brassens imitation or Piaf's *'La Vie en Rose'*. After all this, Pierre would get the car out and the pair of them would have a little tour of the villages and try the cafés in Alignant-du-Vent, Roujan, Neffies, Caux, and back to Pézenas.

'If you are interested in trying the snails sometime, just say the word. We always have them cold with Siddo's Mayonnaise,' Pierre said.

'But don't you have to wait until it rains first?'

'No. I just get the hosepipe out and spray the vines, and the snails think its raining and they come out and surrender.'

When McGinn laughed he said: 'How many do you eat in England?'

'Six or twelve.'

'Ah, yes. Of course that's the big Roman snail done with garlic and parsley and butter in the oven. The ones we have are smaller. I always cook two hundred and fifty for the family.'

McGinn looked at him and he had that rather sly gypsy look about him and he realised this, too, was a challenge.

'I can put an extra fifty on for you.'

'Make it twenty-five,' McGinn said. 'I'm not trying to marry your daughter you know.'

It was his turn to laugh, but McGinn foresaw stomach trouble ahead. He just hoped he kept them long enough for the snails to clean themselves before cooking, and that Siddo remembered to put the thyme and rosemary in with the bran.

'Next time I come from England, I'll bring you a bottle of whisky. It's cheaper on the channel ferry - no customs duty,' McGinn told him.

'What is it? Is it wine?'

'It's whisky. Made in Scotland. Spirit. Very strong. Minimum of seven years old.'

'Never heard of it.'

'You've never heard of whisky?'

'It's not wine?'

'No. It is *not* wine. It's distilled in Scotland and sold all over the world.'

'I never buy drinks in the shops.'

'Are you seriously telling me that you've never heard of Scotch whisky?'

'Yes. Serious. I've never heard of it.'

Suddenly it occurred to McGinn that this man, who had no television set, did not go to the cinema, read only the local paper, the *Midi Libre*, which did not advertise scotch whisky, and indeed had never bought a bottle of wine or spirits in a shop in his life, was being absolutely truthful. Everything he drank he made on the farm: the gypsy women visited with phials of *anis* made from distilled wormwood essence and with half of litre of water and half a litre of alcohol (farmers were allowed to use neat alcohol to fortify certain wines, and it was on sale in the supermarket), he made his own apéritif. This was the stuff they used to call 'the green fairy' in Paris before it was banned by law, the drink that killed Toulouse Lautrec, Oscar Wilde and half the writers and painters of France. This home-made *pastis* was guaranteed to blow the brains out, and to make it was strictly against a law, a crime against the French State (which likes to put its own duty on spirits), and carried a heavy fine and jail term if caught. McGinn had also heard it rumoured that if one bought six bottles they gave you a free white stick. So what with the *vin noix* made by skewering holes into young green walnuts from the tree, settling them in red wine for a month or more, then the moonshine *pastis* from the gypsies, their own red, white, and *rosé* wine and *muscat*, the only drink McGinn could think of that Siddo bought was the *mousseux* to have with the cakes.

'I'd certainly like to try it,' said Pierre.

'You can try some now. I have the remains of a half-bottle in the flat.'

McGinn poured him an English double, which the French call a 'baby' (the equivalent of an English single whisky is called jokingly a 'foetus' in the bars), and asked if he wanted water with it.

'No, I'll just try it like this.'

He took a good slug.

'Wow,' he gasped. 'It's marvellous.'

He took a second, contemplative sip and looked at McGinn with that old sly gypsy look. 'How much a bottle?' he asked.

McGinn told him again that it was cheap on the boat because it was duty free.

'Next time you come over, bring six bottles. I can sell this stuff to friends easily,' he said.

McGinn never did bring him more than a token bottle for the farmhouse, but he certainly acquired a taste for the *usquebaugh*. He would never buy one in a bar, not even with a dead pigeon, for the price of a 'whisky' on the tariff sounded high, although it is the equivalent of four English measures, but a 'foetus' cost exactly the same as a half of draught beer or a *pastis*. He did manage to acquire half bottles from the supermarkets, however, and had them stashed around the farm in bins of straw and the pony's feedbag, no doubt ready for that fateful day when the doctors would call *'Que de l'eau.'*

But he had not yet come to that, and one dark night when they had fortified themselves against the possibility of inclement weather, he was struck by a sudden, bright idea.

'Do you like mutton chops?' he asked.

'Sure - but I prefer a leg rather than chops.'

'Ah, *un gigot*.' He gestured to McGinn to follow him to his car.

'Where are we going?' McGinn asked.

'Wait. You'll see,' he said mysteriously. Pierre was up to something: that gypsy air about him, that mixture of cunning and devilment and the sly grin indicated that he was not thinking about his *'souper.'* Pierre was small and wiry, with a shock of strong black hair that would never fall out, the youngest son of a family of wine growers.

Pierre pointed the car in the direction of Béziers, and McGinn asked again: 'Pierre - where are we going?'

'Next left,' he said. He placed his right index finger on the side of his nose, a good French gesture that meant: 'Don't worry. I know what's going on.'

In the gravel courtyard of a huge building, hidden in the gloom with no sign of life, Pierre expertly reversed the car. When the boot of the Peugeot was near the enormous steel doors of the building, he leapt out, opened the boot and removed the secateurs, car tools, two empty wine casks and an old coat and placed them on the back seat.

'Pull,' he hissed, trying to open the huge steel doors which were painted a dull red, a rust preventative, and slowly he managed to open a gap.

'Where are we? What is this place?' McGinn asked as he took the other handle and widened the gap until it was five feet across. There was no need for a reply but McGinn heard him murmur, *'Un gigot, eh?'* at the same time as he heard the first bleating of the sheep within.

They were in the town abattoir.

With a sudden leap, Pierre was over the wooden fence which penned the sheep into groups of a dozen animals. At a rough estimate there were over a hundred sheep in the building ready to take their last walk.

'Quick - get its feet,' Pierre hissed. He was struggling with an enormous animal and had managed to lift it up, chest high, but it was kicking with all fours and bleating loudly. McGinn climbed over the pen and tried to grab its hind legs. With sheep starting to bleat on all sides, this big fat one was really determined to resist arrest, and with a resounding kick from its right foot, McGinn was sent reeling back against the wooden spars of the pen. He looked at Pierre, this little French farmer, struggling with an enormous sheep in his arms. The other sheep, by herd instinct, thought their day had come and the panic of one had communicated itself to all the others, and their chorus of bleats was reaching a grand cacophony which would soon bring the neighbours running from their houses opposite the abattoir, and suddenly McGinn burst out laughing.

The situation was ridiculous; here he was, a professional journalist, holder of the French Government's Press card, with a wine-grower and family man, owner of a farm worth half a million pounds, and they were SHEEP STEALING.

In England, wasn't the penalty for that, HANGING? Or did they just throw the thief in prison for a few years now?

Pierre's legs were beginning to go at the knees and they buckled as he staggered under the weight of this mammoth load of mutton and he appeared to be doing the first steps of the Viennese waltz, and McGinn started to laugh even louder with just a touch of hysteria as he remembered a little verse that old countryman Laurie Lee had once sung to him in a restaurant in Ibiza:

'I'm dancing with wool in my eyes,
For the girl in my arms is a ewe...'

'Nom de Dieu, Peetair... TAKE ITS LEGS'

Any minute now he was going to fall under the weight of the great fat thing, and McGinn had a swift vision of Pierre in hospital with cracked ribs. He was staggering around now with the sheep's head wagging and its feet flailing. A lesser man would have dropped it and gone to the supermarket... but not Pierre. McGinn grabbed its back legs and stopped its feet flailing, and together they pulled it towards the top of the pen and McGinn managed to open the latch with one hand while holding the sheep's feet with the other, and they dragged the struggling mass of wool out of the open gate and humped it towards the open boot of the Peugeot, then managed, with one gigantic heave, to put the bleating sheep in the open space.

Pierre slammed the top down hard and locked it with his key. He leant back on the closed boot, breathing heavily, trying to get his breath back, sucking in the night air.

Suddenly he jerked upright, looking wide-eyed into the open door of the abattoir.

'Merde', he yelled, as he hurtled through the doorway, arms wide, in the direction of the open pen door they had forgotten to close. The other sheep were squeezing their way through in panic, endeavouring to make a swift dash for freedom and one was already heading towards the open doorway of the abattoir. Pierre, doing an imitation of the Pézenas bar owner Monsieur Vacassey, who once played scrum-half for France, tried to bring it down with a rugby tackle, but the sheep did a neat body swerve and gave him the slip, leaving him rolling over in a mixture of straw and dung. As it ran towards the gap, McGinn stood with legs spread wide and arms akimbo, hoping to block the exit and stop the thing slipping through and heading off in the direction of the Aveyron and home and freedom.

Pierre, from his heap of manure, yelled: 'Shut the doors'. But

McGinn couldn't have shut them if he had wanted to. Although he weighed a hundred and eighty pounds and was almost twice Pierre's height, he had neither his strength nor his lifetime's experience of physical work, having always thought that manual labour was a Spanish workman, so he blocked the gap instead.

Sheep are not as daft as they seem. This one saw the only possible opening - between McGinn's legs, and galloped toward it not caring in the least that its action might turn him into a boy soprano. Just in time, he managed to raise himself by gripping the sides of the steel doors and getting a scissor lock on the animal's neck, cutting off its escape route and, hopefully, its air supply. Its next tactic was to pull backwards, trying to free that part of it trapped in McGinn's legs that had meant to be turned into Irish stew or *ragout d'agneau* or whatever - its neck. That was McGinn's downfall.

He fell down - backwards, onto the concrete portico with a thump, ending up with arms and legs flailing the air like a beetle on its back. He heard a shout from within, and learnt a new French swear-word. Pierre was somehow comparing the charging sheep to some private portion of female anatomy. He had had the foresight to close the pen, but not before three others had got through, and he was in the middle of chasing these escapees around in circles when the first one charged towards him.

McGinn had seen the sheep-dog trials on British television on Saturday afternoons, and marvelled at the whistling farmer and his dogs. What they clearly needed here was a highly intelligent Welsh border collie full of energy, instead of a highly-strung farmer full of *pastis*.

He made a grab at the sheep as it made its body swerve (many a rugby player would have admired its skill), and this time he caught it around the neck, but swung under it, like a cowboy using his horse as a shield from Indian arrows, and the sheep actually ran over him before he grabbed its hind legs, staggered up, and manhandled it back towards the pen.

He turned to glare at McGinn, who saw him take a grubby handkerchief out of his pants pocket and wipe his face. The ewe had peed on him in fright as it ran over him, but such were its leadership qualities that the other escapees had followed it into the pen with the help of a swift kick from Pierre acting as gatekeeper, and everything was under control.

Except for the noise: for the panic of those that had escaped and been captured had communicated itself to the others. Pandemonium had broken out in the abattoir. All the other penned sheep had come out in sympathy and were bleating loudly. Any minute now McGinn expected an irate householder from the street opposite to hurry out to see what the disturbance was all about, or hear the well-known Wah-Wah, Wah-Wah of a French police siren that sounds like a donkey with laryngitis.

They hurriedly pulled the great iron doors shut and jumped in the getaway car. Pierre sped out of the forecourt and headed for the main highway and the route back into town. At the little park that contained the Molière statue, he stopped. It was time to go home and call it a night.

'They used to hang people in England for sheep stealing,' McGinn said.

'But it wasn't stealing,' said Pierre. 'For two years the owner of the abattoir grazed his sheep on my land. I asked him three or four times for payment and he just ignored me. The value of one sheep is exactly the amount he should have paid me for the grazing rights, so touché.'

'I see.'

'Don't worry. He won't miss one.'

McGinn stepped out of the car. Pierre wound down the window.

'Sunday then? *Un gigot*. At midday. Don't be late.'

How could he forget? These Sunday lunches had become part of his life in the Midi, and with bachelor-style eating - pâté, sausage, omelettes, salads - during the week, Sundays were milestones, and the intervening space was traversed like a camel crossing the desert. He was speaking only French, for it was several months before the first English appeared on the horizon.

There had been someone English in the town, for the newsagent received one copy of the *Daily Telegraph* and it was out of season. Normally the town had foreign newspapers only during the summer tourist season. McGinn got into the habit of buying it. As a former journalist, the habit of the daily drug dies hard. One day the friendly newsagent introduced him to an old lady who walked two kilometres each morning to buy her *Midi-Libre*. She was one hundred and four years of age. She sported a walking stick and grey whiskers, and looked as if she would be quite capable of fending off adversaries with her stick. He asked her the secret of her longevity, hoping she would say two packets of Gauloises and three litres of wine a day, but she said: 'Hard work. I worked in the fields all my life. Started as a girl of nine and retired at eighty.'

Feeling quite faint at the thought, McGinn wished her, with great gallantry and duplicity, another twenty years, but the thought did not faze her at all and she seemed to accept it as a possibility. A centenarian in a nearby town, asked about her wrinkles, told the reporter: "Young lady, I have only *one* wrinkle - and I'm *sitting on it!*"

After Easter, when the weather became better, the meeting place was on the terrace of the Café Central where McGinn would pass the hour of apéritif, seven to eight in the evening, with Pierre and his Arab friend Ben Aissa from Morocco, and Volo. Volo was of Polish origin, but his French was fluent and so rapid that it was hard to follow. The first time McGinn heard his name, he thought it was derived from *Vol-au-vent*, the savoury pastry dish, but it came from his original, unpronounceable Polish name. McGinn did not know if it were a common sight, a man who is as wide as he is high, but that was Volo, and in silhouette he resembled a beach ball with a tennis ball placed on top of it. Volo on a bar stool looked like a turnip on a toothpick. He was enormous in girth and his trousers looked as if they had been made by a tent-maker who specialised in circuses.

Someone said that Volo had been a beer drinker in the past, but he complained that it made him bloated, so he switched to *pastis*. Volo drinking the tiny glasses of *pastis* was like feeding a lion on meatballs: they disappeared down the red lane with such rapidity that everyone else was perpetually piling drinks in front of them - sandbagging, as the Americans called it.

Volo was a fertiliser salesman, travelling around the various Domaines and farms, taking and occasionally delivering orders.

It was because they were sitting with Volo that evening that Georges Galette stopped. It was the size of Volo's large corporation that caused Georges to halt: here, indeed was a fellow trencherman, a man who would have interesting menus to discuss. Georges loved his food. He was also everyone's idea of a true Frenchman, with droopy moustache, merry eyes and rose-red cheeks. If Georges Galette wasn't talking about his next meal, he was thinking about it, and his habit during lunch was to discuss what was for dinner. He was famous for his short, sweet *vendange* of only three days' grape-picking, always early, before the others started, when gourmet food was incessantly thrust upon the lucky grape pickers who had been selected for this prize *vendange*.

Georges was looking at Volo with envy. Georges himself had a belly that hung like a badge of honour over his belt as if saying: 'Just look at this and imagine all the wonderful things that have gone into it to make it like this' - but compared to Volo he looked like Nijinsky standing next to Oliver Hardy.

Georges shook hands all round, refused the offer of an apéritif, looked hard at Volo and said: 'We must break a crust some day.'

The French phrase, *'casser la croute'*, sounds very ordinary, simple and easy: to 'break bread', to 'break a crust', to 'break fast', but it is nothing of the kind. It can be a meal of munificent proportions, a full-blown *gourmet* feast lasting from seven or eight in the morning until midday, and is often taken at the time of the hunting season, in September or October when the first game has been shot and hung long enough. Georges and his friends were hunters, and to be invited to *'casser la croute'* with him was the local equivalent of a Royal Command.

Volo looked at Georges' belt, appraisingly, noting the blue T-shirt blown out like a yacht's spinnaker sagging over the region of the buckle, then the look became rather scornful. Who was this shrimp inviting him to light snacks?

'When?' Volo asked.

'Soon,' said Georges, pleased. 'I'll let you know in good time. So you are agreed, then?'

This was clearly a challenge, not just an invitation, and Volo had agreed to meet Monsieur Galette's challenge, any time.

'Where?' asked Volo.

'Chez Roger.'

'With?'

'Oh, a couple of old pals, a few of my friends who drink in the bar, the usual crowd.'

They shook hands.

'I'll be in touch,' said Georges, waving farewell.

The 'usual crowd' of drinkists in Chez Roger were what the French call a *'drôle équipe'* - a funny team. Every one of them had fingers, a hand, a foot, an arm or a leg missing. All had, at one time or another, suffered an *'accident de travaille'*, an industrial accident or agricultural accident.

This entitled them to a lump sum and/or a lifelong pension, which enabled them to pass many hours in Chez Roger, where the *patron* was a sympathiser and fellow amputee, having had his toes removed by a combine harvester while sleeping, as a boy, in a cornfield. Entering Chez Roger at the hour of the *apéritif* was rather like going into the limbless ex-servicemen's club. But although a part of each of them was missing, their humour remained intact. McGinn was with them when the first bus-load of Japanese tourists arrived, about to explore Pézenas and its associations with Molière and the theatre.

Two of the Japanese ordered coffees while their thirty companions trooped upstairs to use the toilet facilities. Roger the *patron* made his usual crack: 'I'd make more by charging fifty centimes for using the toilet and giving the drinks away.'

Alfred, one of the regulars who was short of three fingers on his right hand, asked loudly, with a twinkle in his eye: 'Has Molière been in yet?'

The Japanese tourists with the coffees looked sharply at each other and began to listen attentively.

'Not yet,' said Volo, rising to the occasion. 'He said he was re-writing that last act and he'd be here for an *apéritif* about eight.'

The Japanese became animated and consulted their watches. When the rest of the party descended from the toilet on the first floor, much jabbering and consulting of watches ensued, and the bus passengers began to wait in groups on the terrace of the bar, fiddling with their cameras as they waited for the great French playwright to arrive. A sudden shout of laughter from within the bar made them suspicious, and when tentative enquiries in pidgin English deduced that Molière was long dead, they shamefacedly crept back aboard their bus.

Roger had a fit of the giggles when the bus pulled away, so that he was scarcely able to pour the dozen drinks 'on the house' until Alfred slapped him on the back to calm him down. Roger was small and wiry, but tough. He had shown McGinn the .38 revolver he kept in the till. It was to be used against any opportunist till-robber as he made his exit with Roger's takings. Stencilled in letters the same height as the bar sign outside were the words 'MON BAR' just so that everyone would know who was the boss there. For every two drinks a customer bought, Roger gave the third 'on the house'. So naturally it was a popular meeting place and a natural rendezvous for Georges Galette's breakfast.

When the word went out that Georges had fixed a date, and that they were to *'casser la croute'*, starting at eight o'clock in the morning, several customers went into training by not eating for three days before the big event. The French fascination, not only with food but with the discussion of food, is a phenomenon of that country. If the three great tables of the world are French, Chinese, and Turkish, in that order, it is sure that the Chinese and Turks do not spend one tenth of the time talking about it. McGinn had known French friends give a bite-by-bite account of a dinner they ate ten years previously. It was probably summed up by a line of Maurice Chevalier in a film set on the Marseilles waterfront, when not only had the doctor called *'que de l'eau'* but the greatest *patron* of them all was about to call 'time':

'I shall miss the little things of life,' he said. 'Like *lunch* and *dinner.'*

Georges arrived with a van. Inside the van, in vast cane hampers, was the gourmet meal Georges and his wife had prepared the night before.

McGinn began to perspire, helping him into the café with the hampers, and when he revealed the contents, spread on the joined tables Roger had prepared, it reminded him of a *Yulebord* or Christmas Table he had seen in a Norwegian hotel, groaning with every delicacy from roll-mops to rare beef.

'Have a drink,' said Georges, mopping his fiery red face with a huge handkerchief. But what to drink at that time in the morning? Any Anglo-Saxon would have asked for tea or coffee or chocolate, but Georges would have snorted at the mere suggestion: when the 'crust' was broken in France, it was accompanied by a selection of wines. *Pastis* was really out of the question, but McGinn did notice Roger and a couple of cronies giving themselves an appetiser. Champagne? Red wine? Perhaps later. White wine? Ah, yes, a Kir.

'Good idea,' said Georges, and Roger mixed the white wine and *cassis*, the blackcurrant liqueur, and made the drink named after its inventor, Monseigneur Kir, a Bishop of the parish of Dijon.

Looking out of the café window and across the bus terminus, McGinn spotted the figure (and what a figure), of Volo in the distance, wobbling towards him, coat and pants flapping in the light breeze. He turned sideways to come through the narrow doorway of the inner bar and silently shook hands all round, little goatee beard bristling and his pale blue eyes darting from dish to dish on the tables arraigned against the wall. McGinn felt like saying: 'Seconds out', as he shook hands with Georges, and Georges wished him: *'Bon jour, et bon appétit,'* and Volo replied with: *'A vous même,'* - same to you.

Volo accepted a Suze as an *apéritif* and took his seat.

Seated with him at the long table were Henri, a maker of nougat, Michel, a postman from Montpellier, Jacques, a gendarme from Beziers, Josef, one of Georges' fellow *routiers*, Alfred and three of his drinking companions, all friends of Georges. A place was reserved for Roger who would join them from time to time, for he continued to serve coffees to bus passengers who came and went on the terrace.

On the tables were fifteen kinds of crudités: black and green olives, beetroot, radishes, chick peas, potato salad, Russian salad, celery rémoullade, tomato and onion salad, red cabbage, eggs mayonnaise, asparagus and artichoke hearts, leeks in cream sauce, eggs in jelly, grated carrot, gherkins, and cocktail onions. Then there were eight different kinds of sausage and pâtés from the Herault and the Aveyron, with black and white pudding, rabbit, duck, liver and country pâtés, and slices of York and mountain ham, preserved mussels, quail in aspic, *cassoulet*, casserole of rabbit, chicken drumsticks, casserole of pigeon, magret of duck with olives, *ratatouille*, rice with egg, several wild birds: *ortolan*, thrush, partridge, roast quail. Then there were *pizzas* and *quiche* and *croque Monsieur*, and a variety of cheeses and home-made fruit tart.

During the next three and half hours the mountain of food slowly but surely disappeared as the twelve chosen trenchermen ate is if it were the last supper, and Georges constantly urged Volo to replenish his plate each time it was empty. By eleven in the morning McGinn was beginning to flag. So were Henri, Jacques the gendarme, and Michel the postman, content now to nibble a little Roquefort cheese and goat cheese and blue Auvergne and *bleu de Causses*.

The church clock began to chime for midday. It would strike twelve and then twelve again to give one time to count the strokes the second time around. Inquiring the reason for this, McGinn had been told that very few *vignerons*, or country people in general, wore watches: never in the old days and scarcely at all now for they are susceptible to damage when pruning, cutting and chopping. The man in the fields, miles from his village, depended on the clock and was often so involved concentrating on the work in hand that he would fail to hear the first chimes but would pause to count the second lot.

Georges stood up, wiped his mouth on his napkin, and said: 'I must be off.'

'Where are you going?' Alfred asked him.

Volo was half concentrating on the piece of fruit tart in front of him and half listening to the conversation.

'Why, home for lunch, of course. It's midday.'

'Home for lunch?' Alfred persisted. 'But haven't you had enough breakfast?'

'My wife has cooked jugged hare, you see, a favourite dish, and I cannot disappoint her. But...' He turned to Volo who paused with a piece of tart *en route* to his lips, 'You stay on, Volo, my friend.' Volo looked up at him and the piece of tart disappeared and he began to wipe his mouth with his napkin.

'... *et bon continuation*,' added Georges with a smile.

'No, I've had enough, thank you,' said Volo. 'I wasn't very hungry, really. You see - I had breakfast before I came here.'

Georges' red face was a sight to behold.

CHAPTER 2

R EPLETE, McGinn managed to stagger through the bus terminus, which, luckily, was almost devoid of buses because they rarely moved in the Midi during the magic two hours, twelve to two, or eating time. Just as it is impossible to get a cab in Paris during that time, it is equally impossible to take a bus in the Midi. Other buses were running, however, and one, on its way to Lourdes, narrowly missed him as he crossed the main road to the little square containing Molière's statue. He knew the bus was going to Lourdes because it was Italian and the passengers were all whey-faced, their complexions the colour of the lee side of a Duchess's writing pad, for they had had a little message from Nature to tell them that all was not well, and were on their way to see if they could reverse the situation. He envied them in only one small way, they would be able to get draught Watneys beer by the pint in Lourdes: a huge banner announced its sale on a bar in the centre of town, as if it were in competition with the local water. Georges' breakfast had given McGinn a thirst and he thought of English beer as he entered the little park.

Molière looked raffish: moustachioed, with curly beard and long wavy hair down to his shoulders, he could have been a 60's hippie. Put a sword in his hand and it could have been a statue of D'Artagnan.

A pigeon perched on his head, and carefully deposited its visiting card on his left shoulder before fluttering off. How had it survived the hunting season? Perhaps it had taken refuge in town, away from the barking guns, aimed at everything that moved, from robins to squirrels, and some things that didn't move: a favourite target being the STOP sign or triangular *'Cedez le Passage'* sign, which, throughout the Midi were peppered with grouping from 12-bore lead shot. An angry, empty-handed, cold and hungry hunter would sometimes replace the shot with the twelve gauge lead bullet used for felling wild boar, and blast a hole as if to say: 'Don't tell ME to stop or give way...'

McGinn was focusing on the statue's inscription, *'de ses admirateurs'*, when a little boy came up and engaged him in conversation after presenting him with a large Bourgogne snail, horns protruding and slime track activated. He announced he was five years old as the snail crawled over McGinn's wrist, and added that his name was Dominique. He asked: 'Do you eat snails, Monsieur?' McGinn replied that he did, and asked if he did.

'Non, Monsieur,' he replied gravely, *'Je prefer les grenouilles et les délices de mer.'* A five-year-old with a taste for frogs' legs and shellfish must be rare, even in Languedoc. A future Georges Galette in the making, perhaps? A *gourmet* curtain-crawler; a crumb-crusher *cuisine* critic. He refused the return of the snail, saying it was a present from him so McGinn decided to take it on a tour of the town, and popped it into his pocket.

McGinn's snail's tour took him up to the site of the Chateau where a plaque proclaimed that Julius Caesar once lived there and had made it into his 'Fortress'. No sign of his presence or that of the Celts who founded the place five hundred years before the birth of the other J.C. remained, however, for Richelieu had 'razed it to the ground', as the saying goes, in 1633. That was just seventeen years before old Molière himself came on the scene and took lodgings in the house of the local barber, Monsieur Gely, until 1657 when Paris beckoned. What a strange friendship that must have been, the famous playwright and the local barber. Did Molière get all the local gossip from Gely to put in his plays? He certainly didn't chum up with him for a free haircut. The barber's house, now the *Syndicat d'Initiative* is opposite the Hotel de Ville in the cobbled Place Gambetta. It is in this square that the French film makers shoot their 16th, 17th and 18th century films for there is no need to build a set. This unchanging face of France remains as it was built in 1552, and the *Syndicat* have wisely restored and preserved old shop signs: BIBLIOTHEQUE and VINS ET CHARBON.

McGinn's steps took him to a shop which had an ancient television set (circa 1952) in the window. If Molière had been collecting characters for a play he would certainly have put the shop owner and his wife and son in a play. Monsieur and Madam Lemure came from Rheims, where they had spent the war working for the Germans during the occupation, she as a cook and he as a cinema projectionist. His achievement was to install a short wave radio set into the lampshades by the bedsides of prisoners of war in the hospital. Hers was to set the Gestapo Head-quarters on fire.

Their son, whom Madame Lemure always called *'Tresor'*, a gangling, myopic chain-smoker, wore horn-rimmed glasses with lenses the thickness of beer bottles, his eyesight being so bad McGinn thought that, at the workbench, he would require a metal detector to find his screwdriver, yet his achievement was to have mastered the complicated innards of the TV sets and to be able to activate the oldest, most dilapidated set brought to him for repair.

'A snail has just crawled out of your coat pocket,' said Madame Lemure when they met, so he popped it back out of sight and was invited for a *'digestif'* at their flat in the Rue des Juiveries. Madame Lemure produced the figure of a tonsured monk in brown habit, unscrewed his head, and poured an Armagnac. She loved an excuse for a drink and she had a ready smile and a great sense of humour when recounting a tale.

It was Christmas 1943 that stuck in her memory, when she and the assistant cook had tucked in to everything that came back from the German officers' table, taking this golden opportunity to stuff themselves while the heavy drinking was going on. Unfortunately, the Germans, full of the Christmas spirit (probably all the champagne they had stolen from Rheims where several million bottles disappeared), called the cooks in to the dining room and presented them with a plateful of pork chops and bade them sit down and eat them. Filled to bursting point already, the cooks tried to refuse.

'Cotelets. Gut. Essen,' said an *Obersturmbahnfuhrer, S.S.*, and the French girls were forced to nibble away under the benevolent, glassy stares of the feared Hun.

'It was agony, and I thought my stomach was going to burst,' said Madam. 'But we had to force ourselves to eat the chops. I had a feeling that if we didn't finish them he'd reach for his pistol. Talk about killing us with kindness.'

Later in the war when the tide had turned against the Germans, Madame Lemure was arrested and accused of setting fire to the Gestapo Headquarters. She had been seen, according to eye witnesses, entering the building with a flaming torch in her hand. 'Nonsense,' she told her interrogators, 'I am the cook. I was going to light the oven.' Nevertheless the Lemures made a bid for freedom, cycling on one bicycle towards the American lines. They were halted by a canal. She could not swim. He would have to tow her over. But what about the precious bicycle? Luckily he had brought a tool kit. He dismantled the bicycle, threw it over the canal, piece by piece, towed Madame over, re-assembled the bicycle and fled into the waiting arms of Uncle Sam's boys down the road.

'Tresor' appeared suddenly. He must have smelt the Armagnac from the shop. He took a nip and began loading his camera. The town was gearing itself for Mardi Gras, on the last Tuesday of February, and *'Tresor'*, amazingly, was quite a dab hand at photography.

Monsieur Lemure joined them for little tipple. He was very proud of the old TV set in his shop window with its notice: 'The first television set I ever repaired.' It was much later that he began to imagine that he had *invented* television, confusing his early repair work with scientific discovery, and pooh-poohing the idea that a little Scotsman called John Logie Baird had anything to do with it.

When McGinn told them that Siddo was lending him her late father's uniform as a costume for Mardi Gras, *'Tresor'* promised to take a photograph.

McGinn shook hands all round and continued on his tour.

They were selling metre-long wooden torches, ready for Mardi Gras, the kind of flaming torch carried by the mob while storming Frankenstein's castle, and also wigs and masks for the carnival which would herald the six weeks of Lent, when, presumably, fasting took place, although when someone had asked Georges Galette and Volo what they were giving up for Lent they said, 'rhubarb' and 'water' respectively.

The guide book claimed that Pézenas had 'missed the advance of the motorist and the 20th century', but the part about the motorist was not true until the autoroute between Montpellier and Beziers was completed and the traffic diverted from the town which was a notorious bottleneck all summer. Motorists were forced to stop for the night and the hotels and restaurants were full and the bars open until 3 a.m. The town quietened down only after the autoroute was built. Prior to its completion the tobacconists were open until ten p.m. and McGinn noticed a grocer's shop, opposite the Café des Varietés, which had opened at 7 a.m., just about to close its doors at midnight. When he pointed this out to a customer, he tapped his temple significantly.

The newsagent had told McGinn that the old lady of 104 had talked of seeing the Comedie Francaise as a girl. It was in the little theatre on the site of the 1590 Church of the Penitents Noir, sold after the Revolution and transformed into a theatre still in existence, and it was to raise funds for the Molière statue that the Comedie Francaise played there in 1893, just behind the Café des Varietés, and next door to the house Louis XIV lived in just after Molière moved on. The little theatre was crumbling and falling apart, from its curved painted ceiling to the remains of its gas lamps.

The tiny theatre was a sad sight, and McGinn's historical snail's tour of the town ended in the Café des Sports, where two Gendarmes were taking coffee with the owner, Jo, and had placed their *képis* on the round table near the door. He joined two friends, Raymond and Martine, at the bar and told them he had managed to acquire a Gendarme's uniform for the Carnival. Martine said she was dressing as a clown, and Raymond, a cockney bricklayer known also as 'Bash' on building sites, was blacking up as a minstrel. Martine, whose father, Boby Lapointe, had been a local troubadour, writing and singing his own songs, was distributing little posters for a play being put on by the amateur dramatic society she had joined, *'Le Colporteur'*, meaning the hawker or the peddler. Her singer father had been in the tradition of the great French singer-poet from Sète, just down the road, Georges Brassens, a sort of Robin Hood of ballads, the defender of the humble and the misfits of the world. Brassens was a legendary figure in this town where they named streets after troubadours and admired anyone following in the footsteps of Villon and those who sing of hidden beauty, of kindly acts, of friendships and the things in nature which are missed by the busy leaders of the world.

Someone put a Brassens record, *'Les Copains d'Abord'*, on the juke-box, and McGinn was trying to memorise the words when Raymond pointed to the Gendarme's *képis* on the round table. The snail had somehow managed to escape from the pocket again and had left a silver trail around and across both *képis*.

'Time to leave,' McGinn said, paying for the drinks and endeavouring to make a hasty exit.

'Give this poster to my aunt in the house opposite, and ask her to put it in her window. I haven't the time to go,' said Martine.

'Sorry, but we're late for an appointment.'

'Which house?' I called as we hastened out before the police noticed the state of their hats.

'The brown door. Her name's on the plaque.'

When Martine's aunt Huguette came to the door, McGinn said: 'I've been asked by your niece to give you this, to put in your window. Publicity.'

'Ah, yes, she's phoned me about it. I'll get the Scotch.'

'In actual fact,' McGinn said. 'I prefer Armagnac.'

She hesitated, with the poster in her hand. 'Oh. I meant the Scotch, in fact.' She made signs as if sticking the poster in her window by its four corners and McGinn realised she had meant Scotch tape.

'But I'll fetch the Armagnac all the same,' she said, ushering him into the dining room. 'We'll both have one.'

Huguette, the sister of Boby Lapointe, laughed silently as she poured the drinks.

The morning of Mardi Gras started well, a bright February day, sunny but chilly. The short, four months of winter were not yet quite over, so McGinn donned his Burberry macintosh over the magnificent uniform with its silver epaulettes and ribbons and insignia, and the silver scrambled egg on the *képi* denoting his high rank. In the Café des Sports, Jo the *patron* put the finishing touch with a cork moustache. The waitresses, Annick and Marie, watched, laughing, while Jo performed the transformation of McGinn's upper lip with the burnt cork, and then gave him the first drink of Mardi Gras on the house.

For the next half hour he had the experience of watching people's reaction to the police uniform. Some were instantly taken aback at the sight of the ridiculous cork moustache, but did not dare to laugh just in case he was a real policeman. Some saw only the uniform and veered away instead of entering the bar, taking whatever guilt they had with them. They either disappeared altogether or went into the Varietés next door. Teenage girls from the Lycée would come in, laughing, chattering and giggling, then suddenly stop, freeze, straighten up, start to behave themselves with decorum and, because it was their regular café, sidle in, giving McGinn a watchful, half-disbelieving look, and make for the empty tables in the rear of the premises.

He began to suspect that Jo would think he was losing him customers by frightening them away. Some of the ones who shied away were regulars from the alcoholics ward of the hospital around the corner, opposite Louis XIV's old house, drying out and sipping only the occasional coffee or glass of red wine during their 'recreation period' when they were allowed out. One however, William, actually had the effrontery to put the arm on McGinn for five francs. Most of the men were on the tap, naturally, and William had been for years the most successful at putting the nips in, in both cafés, until it was discovered that the cigar-smoking William owned a block of flats in Sète, and after that the supply of five franc pieces dried up and he returned to rolling his own.

'Why are you dressed as a Gendarme?' William asked, pocketing the five franc piece (he marked all his drinks and paid at the end of the month).

'It's Mardi Gras - carnival,' McGinn said.

'Carnival?' he said scornfully. 'You should try living in the alcoholics ward. Every day is carnival in there.'

Two gypsy-looking types came into the bar and one of them glared at McGinn as they took their places at the counter. The other turned to look at him, coldly. Then he heard one of them say: *'Un flic est un flic,'* meaning a cop is a cop, or once a policeman always a policeman, even if he is wearing a funny moustache. Just then Raymond came in, blacked up as he said he would be, and wearing a bowler hat.

'Ingrey's[1] in Chez Roger dressed as a Mexican bandit, poncho, 'tache, sombrero, the lot.'

---

[1] Derek Ingrey, author of *Pig on a lead* and *Me, Vincent and Mrs Blanchard*
(Cheltenham Literary prize and the Somerset Maugham award).

'How would you like to be Chief of Police?' McGinn asked him.

'Why? Don't you like uniforms?'

'It's their effect on other people I don't like.'

'It's Mardi Gras after all.'

'Do you want to swop?'

'OK. But what'll you be?'

'A city gent, if you'll lend me that bowler hat.'

They adjourned to the Rue des d'André and Raymond donned the Gendarme's uniform and McGinn put on his Savile Row suit by Huntsman, a Wig and Pen club tie, folded up a copy of the *Daily Telegraph* (the *Times* was not sold in the town) and with a borrowed, furled umbrella, joined Derek Ingrey, the novelist who had discovered Pézenas and advised them both to live there.

He looked straight out of *Treasure of the Sierra Madre*, and, in fact, greeted them with the famous line from the film: 'We don't need no stinkin' badges.'

Raymond, who was a musician as well as a builder, had a bristling red beard, and the uniform fitted him better than it had fitted McGinn.

'I've got an idea,' he said, dashing out of the bar.

'Well, did you find a studio for a fiver?' Ingey asked.

'I did better than that, I found a house for six pounds a week, two wine cellars, apartment on the next floor and an enormous attic. How long are you staying?'

'Just for Mardi Gras. Off to Nimes tomorrow.'

A teenage girl, sitting with her mother at the next table, who had been listening to them talking English, turned to her mother and said: 'Those two Monsieurs are English.'

'I know,' said her mother. 'They burnt Joan of Arc.'

Ingrey turned to her and said: 'Oh no we didn't. We just provided the recipe.'

The mum with the long memory snorted, got up and hustled her daughter out of the café.

Raymond came in, bearing a length of chain, which he proceeded to wrap around their wrists.

'Right,' he said. 'You're both under arrest and you're coming with me on a tour of the Pézenas pubs.'

The streets were filling with local people, called the *Piscenois* (from

43

Pézenas). When McGinn had first seen the name, on a notice board, he had thought it meant a *piscine* or swimming pool, but discovered later that it was a roman word derived from the Latin *piscenae*.

The uniform convinced the populace that their act was serious, and young girls clutched their parents and called: 'Where is he taking them, Papa? What have they done, Mama?'

'Get me the British Ambassador,' McGinn called out to them. 'Call the Embassy. I will not be treated like this.'

Ingrey grovelled on his knees, sombrero askew, pleading: *'Senor, Senor. Por favor. No prison para me, Senor. Por favor.'*

Their first port of call was the Bar Ideal in the Rue Anatole France, run by Renée, a silver-haired workaholic who opened at seven in the morning and closed at three next morning.

It was Renée who had asked McGinn recently if he liked 'Aye tyoo'. He thought perhaps Renée had spent some time in Indo China and was offering him an exotic dish from the East.

'Is it Chinese?' he asked him.

'Non. Breetish,' he replied.

'I don't think I've ever had it,' McGinn said diplomatically, not knowing whether it was a dish or a drink or some form of opium.

'Aye tyoo. Aye tyoo,' said Renée, irritated that McGinn didn't know what he was talking about. He then explained that he went by invitation every year to Le Havre, and there he was chef for an annual reunion of a group of men who had been in the British Commandos during the war and had operated in flimsy wood and canvas canoes and had blown up all the ships in the harbour with limpet mines and then escaped in their canoes...

Eureka! Renée was talking about the Cockleshell Heroes, and Eureka! again, the exotic dish which he was clearly able to cook but unable to pronounce was IRISH STEW.

'Of course, Renée, *mon ami*, of course I love Aye Tyoo,' he said.

Then any time he wanted to order it for, say, six or eight people, he would be happy to cook it in his kitchen at a cost per head of, say, fifteen francs, perhaps sixteen...?

'Why certainly Renée,' McGinn had said, 'I'll be most happy to bear it in mind for the future...'

So when he walked in, in chains, being pulled by a red-bearded

Gendarme and attached to a Mexican bandit, he guessed immediately that McGinn had not come to order Irish stew, so he set the drinks up on the bar instead. Customers who had not realised it was Mardi Gras sidled out of the bar to go home to hide or for a costume of some sort. Others who did not want to dress up continued to drink up instead.

The next port of call was the Varietés, where Raymond's girl friend, Martine, was dressed as a superb clown, crosses on the eyes, bulbous red nose, floppy flipper shoes, the lot, and if there had been a prize for the best costume she would have won it. A new set of customers on the terrace were surprised to see a bearded Gendarme with two prisoners kiss the clown in the Pézenas manner, right cheek, left cheek, right cheek again, then wrap a bit of chain around her wrist and drag her into the bar for a drink.

So the day progressed, until the *poulain* was brought out. The *poulain* is the colt, the animal of Pézenas. Each village and town has an animal which is paraded at fêtes and carnivals throughout the year. It is an enormous wooden and canvas structure with a tiny head, and inside the frame, holding it by the spars is either the local rugby team or a group of students, the one requirement being that they must be 100% physically fit to take the strain of the day, for this model animal is bounced in and out of cafés, bars and restaurants throughout the day, with the sweating inmates heaving it at times waist high, then shoulder high, then head high, and then they run with it, towards the crowds on the terraces, a frightening sight as it bears down, head nodding, and then it is swung sideways, so that its backside makes the crowd totter back to a safe distance. For a while the animal reigns supreme in the town, and if the doorway of a café is wide enough and high enough, the *poulain* will charge in and up to the bar, where many hands will pass glasses of draught beer under the 'skirt' of the animal to the perspiring occupants.

The music blares out, the popular tunes of the region, and the animal bounces to a throbbing drum-beat. It is carnival time. In Rio de Janeiro, bare-breasted brown girls sway to the rhythm of Latin-American music; in Britain, the 'Tuesday grease' is used up to make pancakes, and in Soho, the waiters run through the street tossing their pancakes in frying pans; in Spain, all the gays wear drag legally - the one day of the year when it is allowed and not classed by law as 'impersonating'. But in Pézenas, a Gendarme with a red beard has taken a bet that he won't stop the traffic with one wave of his hand.

Raymond strode out into the middle of the main street, beard bristling. He held up his right hand. A stream of cars *en route* to Montpellier came to a sudden halt. He turned and held up his hand again and the stream going to Beziers came to a halt. A frightened family man, with wife and two children in the little family car, saw Ray pointing at him. Then, with a flick of the wrist, the 'gendarme' motioned him to drive into the bus station and stop. The scared driver leant over the wheel as Ray strode slowly and carefully around the car, occasionally bending his knees, hands behind his back, like a stage policeman, examining tyres, number plates, kicking the tip of the exhaust. Then he took something from his pocket, wrote on a piece of paper, folded it up, stuck it behind the windscreen wiper and pointed. The driver couldn't get away quickly enough.

Ray then strode back into the middle of the street, waved on the Montpellier stream, then the Beziers stream, and returned, laughing, to the bar to collect his bet.

'What did you write on the note?' everyone wanted to know.

He had folded a stick of chewing gum into the note and written, in French: 'Your exhaust is loose. Try this.'

Throughout the day there had been various floats, pulled by tractors, some advertising local wines and some filled with children in a variety of costumes, being photographed by two local photographers who would display a hundred or so pictures of the children in the windows of their shops the following week for the proud parents to buy as souvenirs. Darkness came early in February and there was a lull in the Carnival in the evening while people went home for dinner, but then it started up again, and the atmosphere had changed with nightfall. There was something eerie about the old buildings reflected in the torchlight, and the groups who walked alongside floats were dressed in strips of coloured rag and wore long masks which became the beaks of birds, worn on the forehead, and watching them and hearing the banging of cymbals and beating rhythm of drums and tin whistles, they could be back in the Middle Ages. The costumes were medieval, and the float which was surrounded by the men and girls in this ancient costume displayed, with horrible fascination, the severed head of a bull.

The black bull's flower-bedecked head was on a large platter and

Tired and emotional, Raymond rests to recover from a hectic day when he 'stopped the whole street with one wave of his hand' during Mardi Gras, the Pezenas carnival.

the flesh had been cut back from the jaw, revealing all the shining white teeth, so that it appeared the bull had given one enormous grin in death and rictus had set in with *rigor mortis* and the horrific smile remained for all the world to see. This float, surrounded by the brightly coloured bird figures with their long beaks, and men and women with masks holding streamers from the float, had about it an air of menace and malignant corruption. It was pagan, and for a short while the Carnival reverted to the pagan festival it had once been. Masked faces veered towards the crowd almost aggressively, as if challenging recognition, which was impossible.

Men and women wore masks, some hideous, some plain but all defying recognition of the wearer for all one could see was the glittering eyes in the eye-holes. Cymbals clashed and tambourines rattled and horns and whistles blared out as the procession continued with the nodding heads of dogs and bears and donkeys and wolves and the wagging beaks of the bird-men and bird-women in their ragged, multi-coloured costumes. Torches flared on the fringes of the group. A young couple slipped away from the mainstream of the marching revellers and melted into the depths of a shop doorway. Behind the procession loomed the church tower with its scrolled ironwork and bell against the night sky. A stray flicker of torchlight momentarily showed the couple in a deep embrace, masks askew, in the shop doorway, musical instruments abandoned, a length of white female thigh, then they were gone in shadow and the procession continued towards the lighted cafés at the far end of the street.

Revellers streamed from the cafés, holding glasses of wine and brandy to salute the procession as it passed and to stare at the bull's head, garlanded with flowers, teeth glittering in the light of the torches. The musicians went into a favourite tune and the crowds danced and thumped their feet to the rhythm. This was the land of wine and troubadours, of Brassens and of Rabelais, a wine-gulping student of medicine who published Pantagruel and Gargantua in the 1530s down the road in Montpellier, of the Cathares and heretics who defied the church and of the Albigensian crusade when the whole populace of Beziers was put to the sword and butchered around the cathedral. Here was savagery, on the evening of Mardi Gras, and the music and song and wine and debauchery and lust as the carnival became Baccanalian.

So the procession passed through the town and around it and the flickering torches disappeared in the distance and the cafés and bars became quieter and there was a second lull in the day when the young prepared themselves for the night's dancing in the *Salle des Peuples*, and a different orchestra would take over. The festival tunes of Languedoc had gone and were replaced by popular rhythms and jazz and the latest dance craze.

Crowds streamed towards the dance hall, queuing for tickets, three or four deep. Ray and Martine suggested they waited a while until the queue died down, so they had more drinks with the young crowd in the two bars opposite the Ghetto entrance and the bought tickets at the door and passed through the lobby towards the crowded, throbbing dance hall, Martine first, followed by McGinn and then... two gendarmes stepped out of the alcove and arrested Ray.

'Where did you get that uniform?' they asked.

'It's borrowed,' said Ray.

'It's an offence to wear a policeman's uniform you're not entitled to.'

McGinn intervened: 'I lent it to him. I borrowed it from a friend.'

Martine hurried back, worried, tearful: 'What's the problem?'

'That's a senior officer's uniform. Where did you get it?' they asked Ray again.

'I told you.'

'Did you steal it?'

'Of course he didn't steal it,' said Martine, almost in tears now. 'The Monsieur here borrowed it from a friend who is the owner of the uniform.'

'And where did the friend get it?'

From behind McGinn stepped Pierre, who, luckily, had seen the incident from the queue and he took the two gendarmes aside and explained that the uniform had belonged to the late father of his wife, and she had lent it for the carnival, and it was being returned that night. There were handshakes all round. One of the gendarmes remembered Siddo's father, the Pézenas Chief of Police, with affection, so Pierre persuaded them to join him for a drink in the nearby café, to toast the Brigadier's memory.

After half an hour in the dance hall Ray said: 'The girls won't dance with me. Scared of the uniform. Let's go back and change or I'll never get a dance.' They went to Rue des d'André just around the corner and he changed back into his original clothes. McGinn stayed behind to make a parcel of the uniform to give to Pierre but as he was going downstairs with it he knocked on the door. He came into the kitchen and gave McGinn a bottle of *pastis*. It was The Green Fairy, the stuff made from the essence of wormwood: *absinthe*. McGinn gave him the uniform.

'I'm sorry it's not as old as your Scotch whisky,' he said. 'You did say that whisky is always at least seven years old, didn't you?'

'Yes. It's matured for seven years before they sell it.'

'Ah.'

'How old is the pastis, then?'

He looked at his watch.

'Three quarters of an hour,' he said, putting the parcel under his arm and preparing to leave.

'By the way,' he said when McGinn had finished laughing, 'those gendarmes said the next time you bring a snail into the bar, keep it in your pocket and don't let it crawl all over their *képis*. They had a hell of a job cleaning the slime trails off.'

Towards the end of March McGinn went to the farm to help Pierre and his friend the Arab, Ben Aissa from Morocco, to graft 650 vines onto American roots already in the earth. It was back-breaking work, especially for someone tall, bending over, stooped double, to tie the grafted vines firmly together. Two days earlier Pierre had been on a demonstration with fifty thousand other *vignerons* to protest at the importing of Italian wine when already the Languedoc was producing a wine lake: so much table wine was being produced that it would eventually be turned into industrial alcohol.

This grafting was the State's answer: the *vignerons* received financial help to pull up old vines and plant a better quality *Appellation Contrôlée* or *Appellation d'Origine* wine which could be bottled and exported.

The American roots were an insurance against attack by phylloxera, the dry leaf caused by a tiny aphid which came from America in 1886 and destroyed the French vines, for the roots were now immune. The Languedoc had been devastated for ten years and in the end the Parisiens had acquired a taste for cheap powdered wine and would not return to the new wine. Later the French Army became the major buyer of

Languedoc wine, the *'gros rouge'*, which must stick in the memory of all French soldiers, who would agree that it was the kind of wine that gave 'plonk' a bad name.

At midday McGinn was surprised to see Ben Aissa go off on his moped, and Pierre sensed that he was wondering why he did not eat with them on the farm. Siddo was the Arab's amanuensis, for he could neither read not write, completing forms required by law for *Carte de Sejour*, his residence permit, and tax forms. She could not, however, write to Ben Aissa's wife and children in Morocco, for all were illiterate, and they communicated by posting taped cassettes.

'We used to invite him to eat with us,' said Pierre, 'but one day we had a deputation of women from the neighbourhood who were protesting to Siddo that she was making a grave error of judgement by inviting an Arab workman to eat with us when there were young French girls in the house. Siddo was shattered because she is fond of Aissa who is a respectable married man with a family of his own, and he is fond of our children and they love him. But we knew it was a warning and something might be done to Aissa as a reprisal, so we agreed to maintain the friendship at a distance.'

'So it's racism.'

'Sure. It's everywhere - a certain mentality. You think you're a foreigner here? Some of them look on *me* as a foreigner because I come from Montpellier.'

McGinn had to laugh because Montpellier was all of thirty kilometres away.

'Wait until you see the conditions Aissa lives in. We'll pay him a visit.'

They drove out later to the Domaine where he worked, the fields all around in immaculate order, kept in trim by the Arab *smicards*, or minimum wage earners, who lived there. Grape pickers also earned the SMIC, as it is known, the letters standing for *Salaire Minimum Inter-profession de Croissance*, and are often given the same rough and ready living accommodation.

Aissa showed them around: the bedrooms were bare of furniture with the exception of an iron bedstead with a straw palliasse and a couple of Army blankets. The men appeared to have no possessions apart from a transistor radio and the clothes they stood up in. The kitchenette had a cold-water tap over a dirty, greasy sink. They shook hands with an elderly Moroccan and two younger men. They were friendly, hospitable, offering wine and producing two cracked tea-cups. Pierre, having lunched well, was in a merry mood, laughing and joking with the Moroccans, who were regarding him as if he were a visiting doctor or celebrity. They began jabbering excitedly in Arabic with Ben Aissa. McGinn tried to follow what they were saying to him, for he was looking rather furtive and guilty about something. Then a word came which he recognised: *mechoui*, the Arabic for a feast when they barbecue a whole sheep over charcoal. Suddenly he realised why Ben Aissa was looking embarrassed: he had told them about the sheep from the abattoir.

'What's going on?' Pierre asked.

'They're asking me to ask you,' said Aissa, lowering his eyes, 'to get them a live sheep.'

'You told them.'

'I'm sorry.'

'No matter. I can't get them one.'

It was clear they wanted to perform the ritual slaughter with the animal, cutting its throat and bleeding it into the earth to tenderise the meat.

'You'll have to buy one from a sheep farmer,' said Pierre to the Arabs, and they nodded their heads rather disconsolately in agreement, looking crestfallen, and then seemed to lose interest in our presence and sidled off to their own rooms.

'Show us how you communicate with your wife, Aissa,' said Pierre, and Aissa produced a tiny cassette player. Pierre took it, switched it on, took a slug of wine, and spoke: 'Bonjour, Madame, this is Pierre speaking, a friend of Aissa and I have an English friend here and we are going to sing you a little song.' He launched into his version of *'Ma Normandie'* and handed McGinn the microphone and bade him sing *'en Anglais'*.

So McGinn gave a rendering of 'Danny Boy' and tried to imagine the poor woman's face when she switched on her weekly 'letter' from Aissa and heard their attempts at singing. When the little machine was switched off, Pierre asked Aissa: 'When will the asparagus be ready?' He knew that the *patronne*, the woman owner of the Domaine, had made her workmen do unpaid overtime planting a field of asparagus and it was a very sore point with them.

'Two months.'

'Every pay-day the *patronne* cheats them out of the *centimes*,' said Pierre. McGinn saw that look of devilment in his eye and thought that *Madame la patronne* had better watch out.

Pierre dropped him off in the town, and no sooner had he entered the house than he heard the sound of verbal combat in the street below. A girl of about eighteen, intent on driving up the narrow Rue des d'André to the chateau on the hill, was being told that her Austin Mini, the latest British model, would never make it because the street was too narrow.

'Leave the car here and walk,' one of the women neighbours was advising her. 'Take my advice.'

'Walk? I'm not walking anywhere.'

'But the street is too narrow.'

'Nonsense. My car will get through there.'

'You are being stupid, Ma'mselle. Your car, small as it is, will not get up that street.'

'Don't call me stupid, Madame. I know my car better than you.'

'I advise you not to try it.'

'Out of my way.'

She jumped in her little car and revved up. Then she tore up McGinn's street, under the window, and S-C-R-U-N-C-H... the car was jammed tightly between two ancient walls.

Amazingly, she managed to clamber over the seat and squeeze through the back door, and, weeping and bawling, came staggering towards McGinn. He helped her into the apartment and offered her a cup of tea.

'You're English,' she said, accusingly, as if he had been responsible for manufacturing Minis that were too wide.

'Yes,' he said, for he had learnt never to argue about this. If one said 'Scottish' or 'Irish' or 'Welsh', the French would snap: 'Same thing.' If you argued they said: 'You all speak English,' but if you pointed out that the French and Belgians spoke French so 'you must be Belgian,' they would become infuriated, saying: 'Don't call me a Belgian.'

'Milk and sugar?'

'No sugar.' She burst into tears and sobbed into her cupped hands. 'Oh, my poor little car. My baby.'

'Now don't worry. A garage will drag it out and repair it.'

She jumped up, went to the window and looked down on the concertina that had once been her car.

'I was sure I could get through there,' she said.

'You should have breathed in.'

'It's not a joke. Oh, what shall I do? And it's an English car.' She brightened and looked at McGinn as if his nationality allowed him to wave a magic wand and restore her Mini to its pristine state. Then a second thought occurred to her and her sobs became louder: 'They charge twice as much to repair an English car as a French car,' she wept. Suddenly she stood up, resolute, pushed her cup aside and strode out, calling over her shoulder: 'I'm going to the garage now.'

He watched from the window as she took one last, lingering look at the wreck, then she descended to the archway where the neighbour said: 'I told you, didn't I?'

'Shut your gob, you old cow,' was her last cry as she staggered off to get help.

Lord Byron first said, 'No good ever comes of good advice,' and Oscar Wilde took it from him and made it his own. McGinn saw his neighbour and her friend laughing fit to burst, and he knew that both phrasemakers were wrong about good advice.

When the weather became warmer, sometimes McGinn would take a picnic to the little municipal park which was a haven away from the midday bustle of the town, and one day the head gardener approached him. 'Monsieur - don't you have a house?' he asked solicitously, as if commiserating with him for being homeless.

'Oh, yes, in Pézenas,' he replied. 'I like to eat in the open air.'

'Ah, I see.' He seemed not to comprehend why anyone should want to eat *pâté de campagne* and camembert and bananas and drink white wine by a lake filled with gliding swans when they owned a house. 'You're not from these parts?' he asked.

'No, England.'

'Ah, I see,' he smiled, satisfied that only mad foreigners would rather eat under the sky than under a good solid roof.

If it rained heavily, as it often does in the Herault, flooding the rivers and often the villages and towns as well, with a downpour called an *'orage'*, McGinn stayed in the house, but afterwards he would walk for miles through the vines. After rain the evenings were beautiful, with the sun on the bright wet leaves in the vineyards. Looking down from the bridge that crosses the River Herault, he thought he saw fish rising for an evening hatch of flies, but the circles were made by the raindrops falling from the leaves of the trees that overhang the old, calm Herault, as if the trees were weeping into the river.

Each afternoon he took a different direction out of the town. Once off the roads everything became peaceful. There were fields of green feathery flora which appeared to be overgrown asparagus, an ivy-covered wall of a house with nasturtiums growing along the top of the wall, like orchids in the sunlight. When the grapes grew bigger they shone where the surface dust had been rubbed off by the rain and the fluttering leaves, and there were fields of honeydew melons, and cornfields where the vines had been taken up. By the Domaine de Plaisance another ivy-covered wall was light green against the soft brown of the stone beneath, where cement had crumbled away, and half of the wall had been washed by the blue Bordelaise they spray on the vines against blight, making a superb blend of colours and turning the wall into a subject for a painting.

At the ancient watermill on the Herault, red and black lines mark the dates when the river rose and flooded the fields and the town throughout the century. On the other side of the river McGinn carved his initial on the stone at water level by the ruined water pumping mill which once irrigated the fields around. There were peach trees in the field nearby and in Spring it looked like a field of snow, the ground covered with soft white fluff from the trees, blown over the furrows, the apple blossom out on the row that lined the wall, and wild white flowers filling the gaps in the distant vines.

There were wild leeks in the vines first, and then Spring brought all the flowers of the Languedoc out: wild daffodils and gladioli, gentian and cowslip, valerian and bee orchid, purple saxifrage and sorrel, and lavender and sage.

For years McGinn had wanted a garden, and so he decided to move out of town to one of the villages and settle there.

In all the months he had been in the town, he had scarcely spoken English so it came as a surprise when he went to buy his newspaper one morning and the shopkeeper said: 'It's been sold, Monsieur.' For some reason the shop received one copy of the *Daily Telegraph*. Possibly someone had ordered it in the past and the order had never been cancelled, and it was the only English language paper on sale out of season.

'Who bought it?' he asked.

'The other Englishman, Monsieur,' she said. 'He has bought a little house in Castelnau de Guers.'

McGinn knew that the little newspaper van came from Agde railway station at about ten a.m. and so he was there next day and bought the newspaper as it went on display. Then he took up position in a shop doorway nearby and waited. About ten minutes later McGinn saw him. He was unmistakable. The 'other Englishman' wore sandals with grey socks and long, flapping khaki shorts, a grey shirt open at the neck and horn-rimmed glasses. His freckled face had just caught the sun, and his mousy hair flopped over his forehead. He padded along, through the gardeners' market stalls, carrying a string bag that contained one cauliflower. He stopped briefly to check the prices of the oysters and mussels on the stall which received a daily delivery from the Bassin de Thau, the shellfish beds near Sete. His next stop was the newsagent's shop. Within seconds he came out and stood on the pavement, consternation on his face, looking around like a myopic meerkat, clearly shaken by the news that 'the other Englishman' had bought the newspaper.

As he was about to walk away, crestfallen, McGinn approached him, with a wave of the rolled-up *Telegraph* to ensure he could see it clearly, and called out: 'Good morning,' and saw him gape and almost drop his string bag. Then he walked quickly on, seeking the sanctuary of the Ghetto.

During the twelve months McGinn had resided in the town, he had kept a journal with some nature notes on the Herault region. The three cold months were December, January, and February, but the gardeners planted lettuce, broad beans, onions, garlic, and, towards the end of February, early potatoes, just about the time the blackthorn and almond were in blossom and the wild leeks grew in the vines and there was watercress in the streams. By the first week in March the daffodils were out and the first tulip leaves showing, and in the market they were selling primroses and primulas, seed potato and strawberry plants, mimosa trees, roses and dahlias for planting. In the second week of March they planted melons under plastic strips, and bees were active in the rosemary flowers and on the first peach blossom and the white and purple irises that grew by the sides of the vineyards.

A haze of wood smoke hung over the fields: men burnt out the ditches and used home-made petrol drums on pram wheels to burn the *'sarments'*, the vine stalks that are pruned off the main *souche*. The temperature varied between ten and twenty-two degrees and it was possible to sunbathe on a terrace one day and huddle near the log fire the next. March could be windy - not as windy as the Aude, down towards the Pyrenees, a good place to live the French say, if you own a laundry - and it can cut through the narrow village streets and get behind the shutters and chill the bones.

In March the trout fishing season starts, just at the time bluebells and cherry blossom are out. The first swifts appear in the second week and fill the sky by the end of the month when mountain ash is in bud, the gorse bushes turn yellow and dwarf hyacinths appear in the hedgerows. The first cherries are out in the middle of May, closely followed by early strawberries and asparagus.

The butterflies which had first appeared in the middle of April were now in their thousands, for the *vignerons* do not use the insecticide of Northern Europe. The summer is a time of fêtes, and every village and town has one. The work in the vines is sulphating, and if it rains, it has to be done again. By the end of August the farmers are planning the *vendange* and getting teams of cutters and bucketers and porters together, for it usually starts around the end of the first week in September and lasts for three weeks.

After the *vendange* it is the hunting season, for partridge and wild boar, and the mushroom hunting season in the woods, and then a time to play tombola in the cafés and go early to bed, and prepare for the lonely and utterly boring job of pruning the vines. Distant figures can be seen in the vineyards, snipping away through January and February, listening no doubt for the chimes of the distant clock, caught on the wind and lost, pausing for the second count...

Christmas as a celebration is a quiet, family affair, and is over in two days. New Year's eve is a *reveillon* when an all-night feast takes place to bring in the new year with the richest of foods: caviar, lobster, smoked salmon.

There were various sights McGinn had seen, during the time spent in the town, which were unforgettable: a gendarme on point duty being kissed three times on the cheeks by his 18-year-old son off to do his military service, something he could never imagine a British Bobby doing, and Alfred, the customer at Chez Roger who was short of three fingers explaining it: 'The northern people are cold. Here, we are warm: we touch, we hug, we kiss, and why not? Are we not human? Is it not natural to embrace each other?' The sight of two groups of schoolgirls from the Lycée, approaching each other in linked-arms formation, girl number one kissing the opposite girl number five, once, twice, three times, stepping to the left and following the same procedure with girl number two, then three, four, and five until all had kissed. Then they passed on, strolling and chatting, arms still linked.

Sometimes it can be irritating, however. Driving through the town, two groups started to cross a zebra and recognised each other before they reached the middle of the road, where they stopped to chat. Two related families of aunts, uncles, grandparents and children began the kissing and then the chatting. The sun beat down; butter was melting in the car, meat going bad. When the horn was tooted they glared around: who was daring to interrupt this family reunion? They reluctantly parted, calling invitations to lunch, to dinner, to birthday parties.

A wedding party going by, dozens of motor horns in the cavalcade blaring in celebration, the blushing bride waving, and a cynical farmer - possibly a rejected suitor - saying: *'Regardez ça! Aujourd'hui elle est en blanche, demain elle enfanter.'* 'Look at that - today she's in white, tomorrow she'll give birth.'

In winter the bars became rather *machismo* working men's clubs, filled with card players. A woman who entered received many stares and some glares, even if she had come in merely to buy cigarettes. In the old Bar Idéal, where René the insomniac was working like an automaton, the room was filled with card players, grape farmers and their workmen, some Spanish, a few Algerian and Moroccan. Sensible to the needs of some of his elderly clientèle, René the maker of 'Aye tyoo' or Irish stew, had attached a chain behind the door of the toilet for elderly clients to hang on to whilst lost in thought.

These French toilets, known to generations of British tourists on the continent as 'squat bogs' were an out-dated, uncomfortable invention, presumably for hygiene purposes but McGinn had a recurring nightmare of driving through France on a rainy, stormy night, and stopping to use these facilities where, as often as not, there is a 40-watt light bulb on a sixty-seconds time-switch called a *'minuterie'*, which is meanness incarnate, and, as the light goes out hearing the car keys fall down the hole.

Few bar owners had René's sensibility in providing a chain behind the door to aid rheumatism and balance, and a little Spanish workman, perhaps even the original manual labour himself, had gone in to use the facilities but had not bothered to lock the door. A huge farmer, suddenly taken short, hurtled through the bar and grabbed the knob of the toilet door and pulled. There was a startled yell, and the little Spaniard came flying out on the end of the chain, like a Rumpelstiltskin, with trousers at the half-trail, and went sailing through the air to crash across the nearest card table, scattering coins and cards, players and ash-trays, chairs and coffee cups. René dashed forward to help clear up the mess while the Spaniard adjusted his dress, and the bar clients, not knowing whether to laugh or cry, hid titters behind hands and held their stomachs with mirth.

That was the only night the card players who had their game so rudely interrupted decided to go home early for *'souper'*. But before leaving Pézenas for village life, McGinn presented René with a walking stick. He thought it was a present for his old age until McGinn explained that it was to hang in the toilet for customers to use to press the light switch every sixty seconds when it went off during operations.

He enjoyed the joke, and a month later he died, and the new owner installed a modern toilet with a 75-watt bulb.

CHAPTER 3

THE first sight McGinn saw in the village he had chosen to be his future home was a farmer with a horse and cart, and on the cart were two ancient petrol drums, and stencilled in fading letters on them was the word: VERMACHT. The farmer had been using them for carrying diesel oil for over forty years, for they had been left behind by the departing German army. It was indicative of the economic way of life of the people: they threw nothing away; they ran old vans until they dropped to pieces, then they picked up the pieces and put it all back together again for the next *vendange*. It was said that they all had two houses - one to live in and one to keep the rubbish in. The horse was also an economy, for feeding a horse was cheaper than buying petrol, but it was one of the last in the region. Pierre had borrowed a horse once to plough a field, and one was being used a few miles away in Roujan for the harvest, but that period of the seventies and the eighties saw the disappearance entirely of the horse and cart, and the advent of the new, huge grape picking machines which were worked at night as well as during the day, something a human grape picker could not have done.

The building McGinn had bought, for what the local people considered an outrageous price, was an ancient *'remise'*, a word which is translated as 'coach house', or in modern parlance, a garage, a place to keep the tractors and the fertiliser and the farm tools. It was, in fact, wine-making premises, with an ancient circular mill that had actually used a mill-stone, and *'cuves'* to contain the wine.

These wine *'cuves'* were to be opened up for use as rooms, but an exploratory test showed the wall of two of them was 80 centimetres of stone and brick wall faced with concrete on both sides and another, the most recently built, dated 1939, was of reinforced concrete, and days of work with the pneumatic drill would be necessary to force a way in.

The neighbours cocked an ear to the sound of the drill, and the word went around the village: the foreigner was cutting his way into the *cuves*. They knew something McGinn did not know: when you hire a pneumatic drill in France they will tell you, 'Oh, it only costs two hundred francs a day,' but what they fail to say is that that is only the drill itself. Each extra piece is charged: the connecting tube for branching into the electricity, each drill bit, and every extra until the amount is doubled. Then they put V.A.T. and delivery charges on top.

But McGinn had given the villagers an idea: if the foreigner could break into the *cuves* to make them habitable, so can we, but we know how to do it quicker and easier and less expensively.

It was the *garde champêtre* who first told McGinn how they were going to do it: they were going to use dynamite.

The function of a *garde champêtre* in a French village is to ensure that everything runs smoothly. He is the village policeman and is supposed to wear a *képi* to show his status. His work ranges from emptying the dustbins into the cart twice a week, trimming trees, building footpaths, painting the clock face and maintaining its works, and generally prettifying the village and handling any emergency such as the water tower not functioning properly or street lights failing. He is always an excellent source of information.

He was wearing his *képi* when he told McGinn about the dynamite. He had come to ask for stones.

It was much later that McGinn discovered why the stones that had been tumbled out of the ancient walls of the *remise* to make spaces for window frames were so valued. Only when it was pointed out by a neighbour with an interest in archaeology that by the doorway was the original Roman arch which was the entrance to the village two thousand years ago did the penny drop. The building contained many cut Roman stones. Not only that but the living room wall was the original ramparts of the village, the first 'belt' of three protective stone walls and contained a cave of Saracen stone that must have been built around the year 700 at the time of the Saracen occupation of the Languedoc. The cave was revealed when workmen took up the huge pine floorboards to lower the living room floor, for there was a one-metre gap between the wooden floor and the ceiling of the floor below where the five *'cuves'* were. In 1939, the owner had built the reinforced concrete wine *'cuves'* into the Saracen cave, leaving the magnificent herring-bone roof showing.

The Romans had built aqueducts in all the surrounding valleys to take water to Beziers and over the years builders had used this cut stone to heighten or improve their houses in the village. The stones had probably been cut by slaves, for, to the best of knowledge, the Romans did not even pay the S.M.I.C. or minimum wage on building projects of this nature.

The Romans were clever, however, for while the foremen were encouraging their workers with whips, their engineers were constructing an incredible sewage system which still honeycombs the village, and a well that went through the centre of the village which must have been seventy metres deep, in case of siege.

The question was: could today's dynamiters match that Roman skill?

The day of the dynamite dawned fine and clear, as it usually does in the Midi, with cocks crowing, chickens squawking, dogs barking, and the women watching the clock and waiting for the bread van to arrive. The owner of the *remise* to be dynamited was to be present to supervise operations, personally placing the charges in accordance with his plan to make the ground floor into a living room and the upper floors into bedrooms. His basic plan was to blast one big hole, big enough to make French windows in the reinforced concrete of the main wine *cuve* and that would be the entrance to the living room. Simple.

McGinn's little team of builders, consisting of Raymond, the cockney bricklayer and late 'gendarme' called Bash; an English plumber, Tom Burton; an electrician called Ginger, and an odd-job man called Dave. All expressed a wish to witness the event. A little black and white dog, which seemed to have adopted McGinn and had been christened T.F. which stood for *Toujours Faim*, or always hungry, insisted on following them up the hill.

The village men had gathered at the building when they arrived. The *garde champêtre*, clearly there in an official capacity, wore his képi. Four village councillors and the Mayor himself had been drawn there by curiosity, and the Mayor had donned a jacket for the occasion.

Normally he wore stone-washed blue jeans, a designer T-shirt and a large straw hat, and went off to his fields on the tractor looking like an extra from 'Oklahoma!'

The owner of T.F. was there and he acknowledged her presence with a backward flip of his heel. He was annoyed with her because she absolutely refused to hunt, chase rabbits, pick up fake ducks, flush quail and partridge, and generally behave like a hunting dog. She also fled at the sound of gunfire. She had been found injured on a roadside by the owner's son, and nursed back to health in the belief that she was valuable.

When her pacifist tendencies were discovered, she was ostracised and occasionally thrown a dry crust of bread. T.F. was not a *'chien de sanglier'* as the wild boar hunting hounds are called, but a *'chien de cheminée'*, content to sit at the fireside waiting in vain hopes of the odd pheasant wing being thrown in her direction.

'Do you know how to handle dynamite, Monsieur?' Bash, the red-bearded cockney bricklayer, asked the proprietor of the building where they were gathered.

'Look, Monsieur, I've placed the four charges on the four corners where I want the opening. That's simple enough, isn't it? Once I get four holes through the concrete, the rest can be done with a sledge hammer. Why? Do you know about dynamite?'

'Sure. I've used it on building sites in Rotterdam.'

Tom the plumber and Ginger the electrician winced. Bash had not acquired his name for his finesse. He was probably the originator of the British workman's stock phrase: 'It just come orf in me 'and Guv.'

'And,' Bash added, inspecting the charges, 'these are far too big as charges. You need about a third of the amount you've used on each corner.'

'This is *béton*, Monsieur - reinforced concrete, not blancmange.'

The *garde-champêtre* adjusted his képi to a more official angle. *'Monsieur le Maire,'* he said, drawing himself up to his full height of five foot two inches with his shoes mended, 'Has permission been given for this?'

'You don't need permission for demolition, only construction - unless of course it is a listed building, which this is not.'

'But the church is. It could be damaged by the force of the explosion. After all, it is a twelfth century church.'

'I thought it looked a bit old,' said Bash the bricklayer with a twinkle in his eye. 'I'll pebble-dash it for you if you like - for a price.'

Some of the councillors saw the joke and tittered, but the *garde-champêtre* was not amused.

He turned to the Mayor: 'Have you checked with Montpellier about this?' he asked.

The Mayor, once a carefree, kindly, affable man, now weighed down by complaints on all sides and worried by the cares of office said, briefly: *'Merde a Montpellier'*.

'But shouldn't we evacuate the people in the houses left and right, in case of accident?' the *garde-champêtre* persisted.

'You could issue them with tin hats,' said Bash, whose fluent if slightly ungrammatical French he had picked up on many grape harvests and building sites.

'I know all about your tin hats,' said the *garde-champêtre* darkly, referring to an incident when Bash was caught by the gendarmes wearing an old German helmet instead of a proper motorcycle helmet.

'That doesn't pass here,' the gendarmes told him.

'It passed in nineteen forty, mate,' Bash had replied.

'Look, this is building work, not an unexploded bomb,' said the Mayor. He looked at the church clock. 'I suggest you get on with it.'

The shutters in the house behind where the group of mixed councillors and foreigners stood were suddenly flung open, and an angry face glared out of the gloom within: she was about seventy years of age with straggly grey hair and she was waving a walking stick.

'It's all right for you foreigners,' she screeched, 'You've got the money. My house is falling down, but I can't afford to repair it. Not with the prices builders charge.'

Bash looked up at the angry cadaverous face at the window: 'Madame - I'll repair it for you - for half price,' he called.

'You shut your big mouth and go back to your own country where you belong,' she screamed.

'There's no need for that abuse, Madame,' called out one of the village councillors, a portly, red-haired man, 'a little *politesse* if you please.'

'You shut your big mouth too - foreigner,' she yelled.

'What do you mean, "foreigner" - you old bag. I am French. I was born in Beziers, fifteen kilometres away.'

'Foreigner. Foreigner. Go back to Beziers,' she shouted.

'Desist,' shouted the Mayor, glaring up at the open window. 'That's enough insults from you, Madame, if you please.'

'You're a foreigner too,' she screamed, waving her stick at him. 'You look like one.'

His dignity affronted, Monsieur le Mayor drew his shoulders back and called: 'That is an insult to my family, Madame. The dead generations of my family lie buried in that cemetery right there.' He pointed to the ancient village cemetery no longer used but still consecrated ground.

'Call that a cemetery,' she shouted. 'It's a disgrace. Look at those crosses lying around everywhere, rusty, rotten, and dogs scratching around everywhere.'

Suddenly T.F. barked at her: once, twice, three times.

Everyone started laughing.

Bash addressed T.F.: 'Shut up - foreigner,' he yelled.

A roar of laughter went up from the *vignerons* and the councillors, and even Monsieur le Mayor himself forced a bleak smile.

Mortified and defeated by laughter, the widow gave one last angry glare at the throng below and then bent through the window frame, pulled the shutters and slammed them hard. Some flinched, for there is no sound quite like the insulting finality of a French widow slamming the shutters in your face.

'Let's get on with it,' said the owner of the *remise*. 'Stand back, everyone,' he called as he made to enter the building.

'I don't think you should light those fuses, Monsieur,' Bash called out to him. 'I've told you - the charges are far too big.'

'Nonsense. I know what I'm doing. This is my property. Out of the way, everyone, I'm going to light these fuses.'

He strode towards the dynamite purposefully, lit the fuses and then came running back, shouting: 'Get back - everyone get back.'

All moved back against the wall of the angry widow's house and waited, counting the seconds: eight, nine, ten, eleven, twelve. Suddenly, with a shattering roar, the dynamite went off, like four gas bottles exploding at the same time, and this was followed by a tremendous crash as the floor above caved in. They watched, aghast, as, with a slow creaking of timbers and a final cracking sound, the beams began to fall and the tile roof caved in and a cloud of centuries old dust rose from the mount of rubble.

T.F., with one yelp, shot off like a bullet.

There followed a great silence, then they heard the widow's voice reciting, almost pleading:

'Holy Mary, Mother of God,

Pray for us sinners, now,

And at the hour of our death...'

'Anyone want to rent a windy pick?' asked Bash.

'Back to the drawing board,' said Dave the odd-job man.

'Now that is what I call creative demolition,' said Ginger the electrician.

'Anybody want to buy a plot of land?' said Tom the plumber.

'Time to go in,' McGinn said diplomatically before being asked to translate their remarks for the village council. They were just behind the *garde-champêtre* on the little hill leading down to the house, for he was hurriedly removing his *képi* and doing a disappearing act in case there was any clearing up work to be done.

'We shouldn't laugh, really,' said Bash, holding his sides with silent mirth.

'Oh, I don't know,' said Ginger, and the bottled-up laughter came out like a gale. One of the village lads, Henri, was in the house as they entered. He often visited, asking for Marlboro cigarettes, which appeared to him to be the height of sophistication at three times the price of a packet of Gauloises.

'What was that noise?' Henri asked. 'It sounded like an explosion.'

'Somebody lit a match in the toilet,' said Bash. 'You know what these French farts are like.'

Tom the plumber, who was a dab hand at carpentry, had built three steps from scaffolding pine and placed them at the entrance to what was to be the open-plan bedroom, just on the left of the staircase he had built to the floor below where the wine *cuves* were. Their position was temporary and Tom had placed a brick behind the lowest step to stabilise them.

McGinn started to climb the steps and suddenly they gave way beneath him and the steps shot sideways and he fell in the other direction, down the newly-built pinewood staircase, turning and clutching at the banister for support and managing to grab it twice to break his fall before he hit the concrete below.

Falling downstairs is an extremely painful experience, and McGinn was picked up, helped back upstairs and given a cup of tea by Bash and Ginger.

'Who took that bloody brick away?' McGinn asked.

Tom went over to inspect the spot where he had propped the three steps. No brick. He looked puzzled, searched downstairs but could find nothing.

Henri, curious, asked Dave what Tom was looking for, and Dave explained that someone had taken a brick from behind the steps. Henri went to a recess in the ancient wall, a large hole that had recently held an enormous beam before the floor was lowered. He poked his hand inside and produced the brick.

He stood there with a silly look on his face, Marlboro in one hand, brick in the other as they turned to look at him.

'You stupid...' Bash never did finish what he was saying, for Henri dropped the brick, whimpered: 'I was only trying to tidy up,' and scampered up the stairs, through the kitchen door and out to join his teenage cronies on the steps of the Marie.

'Let's call it a day,' McGinn said. 'I'll see you tomorrow at eight.' But Tom the plumber said he couldn't make it.

'I may be late. I've got an ordered job. I can't ring you, can I? You should order a phone now because there's a waiting list in these villages, and you sometimes have to have a shared line. Just ring Telecom at Beziers.'

Ginger said: 'By the way, I have to get wire, plugs, the electric wall heater, so can you meet me at the shop in Pézenas? I'll go in on the motorbike first thing.'

'OK, Ginge, I'll meet you at the shop,' McGinn said, 'and get everything on a cheque.'

Next day at the electrical shop there was no sign of Ginger. McGinn waited for half an hour then began to search the cafés for him. He found him in Café Vacassy, the rugbymen's bar. He was standing at the bar, with his hands placed firmly on the zinc counter, as if trying to steady himself. Surely the normally abstemious Ginger couldn't be drunk at this time of day?

'Are you all right, Ginge?' McGinn asked, joining him.

'Sorry I couldn't make it,' he said out of the side of his mouth, 'but I'm in a fix.'

'What do you mean?'

'Look slowly and carefully behind you. That motorcycle policeman. He's drunk,' said Ginger, grasping his own coffee cup.

'So what? It's not your fault. What's it got to do with you?'

'But don't you see - I'm on my motorbike. It's outside the door there, right next to his. If I try to get on it, he can breathalyse me.'

'But you're drinking coffee.'

'Now, yes, but I had three *demis* earlier and I'm over the limit. Met Michel the postman and he started buying as he'd been on night shift. I've been trapped here for an hour waiting for that bugger to leave.'

The motorcycle policeman was certainly the worse for wear. He sat slumped with his chin on his hands, staring at Ginger's back.

'He doesn't look capable of breathalysing anyone at the moment. He'll get done himself if his colleague comes in.'

'That would be funny,' said Ginger. 'One cop nicking the other. He must have been invited to *"casser la croute"* somewhere.'

'Anyway, let's go, Ginge, and get that wire. You can pick up your bike when he's gone.'

'I can't do that.'

'Why not?'

'Because he's got my bloody helmet.'

McGinn looked again and, sure enough, on the table in front of the drunken policeman was Ginger's helmet, black, but marginally different by having two tiny red arrows on the sides.

'Watch him. He keeps trying to get it on,' said Ginger.

McGinn ordered two coffees from the barman and turned slowly to watch the member of one of the most feared police forces in Europe, the *Corps Republicain de Securité*, take his face out of his hands, look puzzled, pick up Ginger's helmet, and try to squeeze it onto his head, as if in severe pain, screwing up his eyes and pulling the sides of the helmet down towards his ears. It was like trying to squeeze a rugby ball into a tea-cup.

He screwed his mouth up and squeezed even harder, but finally gave up, pulled Ginger's helmet off his head and sat staring at it as if to say: 'Funny, it's shrunk.'

'His own helmet,' said Ginger, 'is hanging up on that hat-rack in the back of the bar where he put it when he came in.'

McGinn looked into the gloom where the silent juke-box and games machines were, and there was the shiny black helmet hanging by its strap.

'You have to switch helmets, Ginge,' he said.

'How can I do that? He's not so drunk as he wouldn't notice.'

'There's only one way: distract his attention long enough to make the switch.'

'How do we do that?'

'We need a topless barmaid, a stripper on the bar or a Canal-Plus blue movie on the TV.'

Ginger laughed, then turned serious. 'I can't leave without it. I don't want to have to buy a new one and I can scarcely take it off him. He might shoot me.'

'I'll grab his gun and you kick him in the cobblers.'

When McGinn saw Ginger was no longer laughing, he said: 'I'll go to the post office round the corner and phone the barman and ask for the C.R.S. man to come to the phone. You dive back in there, grab his helmet, switch it for yours while he's listening out of sight round the corner there and Bob's your uncle.'

'I suppose it's worth a try, anyway. I can't stay here all bloody day.'

McGinn rang the café from the P.T.T., asked for the police motorcyclist and kept him holding on the line long enough for Ginger to make the switch, then walked through the town to meet Ginger at the Varietés, as pre-arranged.

'The only disappointing part,' said Ginger when they met, 'is that we couldn't see the look on his face when he finally tried the helmet on and it was a perfect fit.'

'True. But there's one thing puzzles me, Ginge. You say you had three *demis* with Michel the postman. That's not *over* the limit. You're allowed an *apéritif*, half a bottle of wine with a meal and a *digestif* here.'

'Ah, with a meal, yes. But what I had doesn't count as a meal. I had a Rhum Baba.'

'A Rhum Baba? A cake? That's not alcoholic. They put syrup of rum on them, don't they?'

'Not at the shop I go to.'

'You mean to say they put real rum on it?'

'Lashings of it. The two old ladies who run the cake shop have known me for years. I have a Rhum Baba every Saturday during the *vendange*. They keep a bottle of rum Saint James, especially for me, and boy, do they slug it on. About the equivalent of a double in a bar. So I *was* over the limit.'

When they returned with the wire and plugs Bash said: 'There was a Dutch family here earlier, looking for property, being shown around the villages by an old mate from Rotterdam, Spider Smith. They say they'll pay six thousand quid over what you paid for this building, unfinished. Are you interested?'

'Not at all.'

'I told them you wouldn't be. Spider's found a house for himself, in fact two houses adjoining. He wants Tom and Ginge and me to work on them when we've finished here. His missus and kid will join him here from Rotterdam when it's habitable.'

'It's French week next week,' McGinn said. 'Jean-Paul and Patrice doing the plastering and tiling...'

'What? Jean-Paul has managed to escape from his wife again?' said Bash. The French expert at plastering had a jealous wife in Normandy who did not like him coming back to see old friends in the Languedoc where he had a tiny *cabanon* in the vines. He occasionally escaped but she would arrive and search the bars and drag him back to the house he was building for her there when he had been gone too long.

'I hear they're getting divorced soon,' said Tom.

'Is it true,' said Ginger, turning to McGinn, 'that you and Patrice sent him a cake with a file in it?'

'There is no truth in the rumour - as yet, as a newspaperman will say. It's a good idea though.'

'Come off it. Marie-Lise found it when she cut into the cake. She knew it was from you and Patrice or his girl-friend Freddy.'

'Well, if there's going to be a divorce you'd better keep quiet about it. She might use it as evidence,' said Tom.

'Before you go, can we get rid of that sink?' McGinn asked, pointing to a marble sink near the door that must have weighed close to two hundred kilogrammes or the equivalent of four bags of cement.

'Come on - one on each corner,' said Bash, proud of his own strength. 'Where to, Guv?'

'Just by the door. I'm going to use it as a bird bath.'

'What - you mean when you get a bird?'

'No,' McGinn said, when the laughter died down. 'When I build the flower beds by the door.'

'I nearly asked the *garde-champêtre* to ditch that when he came for those stones,' said Bash.

'Ditch it? Ditch it? Why, that's a collector's item,' said Ginger. 'Imagine all the hangovers that have been sluiced away in that by the *vendangeurs* over the years. And that tree by the door is what's called a *vendangeurs'* peach - somebody planted a stone years ago and every year you'll get fruit off it.'

'Grab hold here, Ginge, and stop rabbiting,' said Bash. 'You need a bit more exercise. Getting a beer belly again. You know what the French girls call that, don't you? A Kronenbourg muscle.'

When the sink had been heaved into the street, McGinn said: 'By the way, I would like one volunteer to help me get the plate glass for the terrace door tomorrow.'

'I'll come,' said Ginger, Bash, and Dave.

They laughed. 'We can't all go,' said Bash.

'As the unskilled man here,' said Dave, 'I think it's down to me. Let's not fight about it. You know my aversion to fighting.'

'OK, Dave, thanks.'

'Most happy to oblige, dear boy,' said Dave, 'and, speaking as a gentleman, a poet, a scholar, and a lazy bugger, I'll be most happy to accompany you on the errand.'

'Right, but we're carrying plate glass in the car, so no booze and no "walkabouts",' McGinn said, referring to his well-known disappearing act when he would vanish for days, weeks on end, to the Pyrenees or Marseilles or even as far as Morocco, while his French wife tried to locate him by telephone.

'Perish the thought, dear boy,' said Dave.

He did his disappearing act in Pézenas after mumbling something about 'saying goodbye to a few old friends.'

The paint shop said the six foot length of glass would be ready in an hour. McGinn had forgotten to bring an old blanket to cover it and the shopkeeper provided some old *Midi Libre* newspapers and together they got it into the car. But where was Dave? McGinn needed him to steady it in the back seat as he drove. He was clearly touring the little artisans' shops in the back streets. At each one where he was known they said: 'He only had one glass of wine and left.' So McGinn asked the next shopkeeper, an English girl selling bangles and beads, 'What wine did you give him?'

'Oh, that white one called musc... musc something.'

'Muscadet?' McGinn suggested, hoping it was the dry white wine from Brittany.

'No. I think it's the sweet one - muscatel.'

His heart sank. Dave on muscatel. He eventually found him in a bar near the post office, sipping beer.

'Have I ever recited my poem about Lily Langtry to you, dear boy,' said Dave, pulling up a chair.

'Several times, Dave. You've been mixing your drinks.'

'In the most pleasant way. I had a little walkabout. See some friends. These little shops often have a secret cache of booze about the premises y'know.'

'The muscatel, I hear.'

'Ah, you've discovered my secret. Yes I did manage to combine my farewells with a little *degustation...*' He put his hand in his trousers pocket, withdrew it significantly. 'Forced, as I am, to resort to that in my present state of impecuniosity.'

'It's pay day tomorrow.'

'Ah, but tomorrow, dear boy, in the words of that American lady scribe and philosopher - the name escapes me - tomorrow is another day. As was yesterday. And as will be the day after tomorrow, and in the meantime, do you think you could see your way...'

McGinn gave him a 100 franc note.

'Against wages, dear boy. Now what are you having?'

'Nothing. We have a little job to do - like handling six foot of very sharp glass in my *bagnole.*'

'And where are your wheels?'

'Where we left them, Dave. Outside the bloody shop.'

The journey back was a nightmare.

'If we hit anything now, or you jam the brakes on,' said Dave's doom-laden voice from the back seat, 'that glass will take your head right off.'

'Shut up, Dave.'

'Drive slowly, dear boy.'

'I am driving slowly. Twenty miles an hour, and I'm trying to concentrate on the road.'

'I've seen what broken glass can do in an accident,' said Dave, and McGinn glanced at the edge of the glass which was about eighteen inches from his neck. 'And it's not a pretty sight. It could take your head right off your shoulders, dear boy.'

'Will you shut up and let me concentrate.'

A stream of lorries and cars filled with angry French motorists, impatient as usual, were tooting their horns behind them.

'They want to overtake,' said the voice of doom.

'I *know* they want to overtake, Dave. But they *can't*.'

'Did you know,' said Dave, 'that Napoleon planted the plane trees to shade cavalry?'

'Yes, and Hitler built autobahns to carry tanks - and that's what I'd like to be driving right now.'

'Do you think we could stop for a little libation in Roujan, dear boy? A terrible t'irst has come upon me.'

'Dave, if I stop now I'll never get back in this car.'

At the house, McGinn staggered, jelly-legged, indoors while Bash and Ginger carried in the plate glass. McGinn put the kettle on, went downstairs to inspect the work, and when he returned Dave had disappeared again. 'You didn't give him any money, did you?' Bash asked.

'A hundred francs.'

'Well, that's it, then. He's off on one of his mini-walkabouts - the nearest pub for sure. You won't see him again today.'

During the weekend, Gilles from Brittany came to give a hand building the flower beds. Gilles had a droopy eyelid and when he became excited and voluble the eye flashed and glittered. His nickname was *'Le Pirate'*, and he was the kind of university graduate who gave the word 'dropout' a bad name. He actually worked emptying dustbins and gleaning extra money from his knowledge of antiques and *objets d'art* and was part of the Paris 'ring' of its high-earning garbage disposal teams. He had occasionally met former classmates from the Sorbonne where he had acquired a degree in German language and literature, who were shocked by his new job.

'How,' asked Gilles, 'do you propose to lift that marble sink to waist level? It is impossible without four gorillas or a fork-lift truck.'

'Four of us got it outside.'

'I have it. Block and tackle,' said Gilles, his eye flashing. 'We can use the high branch of the tree to haul the sink up and swing it into place.'

'We need an extra man. That thing weighs 200 kilos.'

'I know just the man. Panique.'

'Panique?'

'The wrestler. He owns a bar now in Roujan and works also in the abattoir. I'll go and phone him.'

Within twenty minutes Panique arrived and shouldered his way into the house. Like Volo, but with muscle instead of fat, he had to turn sideways to enter normal doorways. He had a close-cropped bullet head, hands like mountain hams, a ready smile and one of the deepest voices McGinn had ever heard.

'Where is it?' was all he said, and Gilles conducted him downstairs, through the door and out to where the marble sink stood, near the block and tackle Gilles had rigged up.

'Is that it?' said Panique.

'That's it,' McGinn said. 'If you haul on the rope, Gilles and I will steady it and swing it into position.'

'Excuse me,' said Panique, motioning them aside.

He bent down, legs spread, and grasped the sink on either side, then with one gigantic heave he lifted it to waist level, then placed it exactly where McGinn wanted it on the bed of stones.

'Anything else?' Panique asked.

'No. That's all. Would you like something to drink?'

'Une biere s'il vous plait,' said this man of few words.

He drank his bottle of Kronenbourg, shook hands, and departed.

'There was a fight in his bar last night,' Gilles said. 'Someone picked on your friend Bash.'

'A dangerous thing to do,' McGinn said. 'He can knock half a dozen men out in a row.'

'That's just what he was doing when Panique lay on him. Panique didn't say a word, just lay on him and there was Bash on his back with Panique on his chest, with arms and legs waving like a beetle. End of fight.'

Gilles returned the block and tackle to Monsieur Berger, from whom he had borrowed it. At the same time he borrowed a *comport* - one of the big plastic bins with metal handles for transporting the grapes to the presses. Hitherto all *comports* had been oak, but plastic was replacing them and the oak ones were being sold as rustic flower boxes for terraces. The new plastic bin which Gilles borrowed was to be used for punch, his concoction of wine and cointreau and fruit to serve when the first stage of building was over. The day of the party was put off again, however, for a day at least, when no-one turned up for work on Monday morning.

'It's Lundi Club,' said Gilles.

'So today is cancelled through lack of interest,' McGinn said.

Monday Club was an invention of the British workmen who found occasional work in the area after the *vendange*, some of whom had settled in and around Pézenas.

Some of the French took to it like drowning men to a lifeboat: an excuse to nurse hangovers in the cafés and reminisce on the activities of the weekend. Any *patron* or *entrepreneur* who had the temerity to call for extra hands was abruptly told: *'C'est Lundi Cloob.'*

'We may as well go to the stores and the ironmongers in Beziers today,' said Gilles. 'If you like, I'll drive your car. It's a complicated traffic system: four lanes in and out and one way streets in the centre.'

'You're welcome to drive in that kind of traffic any day, Gilles,' McGinn told him.

He rubbed his hands together and his mad eye glittered. McGinn wondered what could possibly be so exciting about driving in heavy traffic in narrow one-way streets in a town centre. The reason for his enthusiasm became clear as they hurtled down the hill towards the railway station.

His pirate's eye gleamed as he revved up and McGinn suddenly remembered that his ambition was to be a *cascadeur*, a stunt man in films, and his favourite movie was the one where Jean-Paul Belmondo, replaced by a team of stunt drivers, has a whirlwind and nightmare drive in a town which seemed to consist of hilly staircases and steps. Gilles swerved in and out of the traffic, changing lanes as frequently as possible, cutting in front of other cars, racing up to the car in front then jamming on the brakes, scaring the occupants silly, tooting the horn continuously, revving up, shooting lights, racing ahead, slowing to let the others catch up, then carving them up again.

'Gilles,' McGinn yelled. 'What the hell are you doing?'

He turned his droopy eye on his passenger: 'Look at their faces,' he shouted.

'I can see their bloody faces. They're angry.'

'Don't you see? They think I'm an Englishman. It's the number plate and the GB on the back. They hate me.'

There was no doubt that the sight of the GB and the number plate on the Renault, being driven by a crazy, mad-eyed 'Englishman' was sending them in paroxysms of hatred, and from the look of them, waving fists and shouting, they had sworn vengeance. They tried to catch up and they tried to cut in, they tried desperately to overtake Gilles as he swerved and gunned the little car downhill, laughing crazily and occasionally glaring at them as they came alongside. There was a red light ahead. Gilles was forced to stop. The car driven by one of the irate motorists who had been carved up by Gilles crunched to a halt alongside and the driver wound his window down. They could hear his yells even through the closed windows:

'Bloody stoopid Eenglish - where you learn to drive, eh?'

The lights changed. Gilles gunned the car and took off at the same rate of knots towards the next set of lights.

'Ha ha. You see? He thinks I'm English,' he shouted.

It was at the next traffic lights that McGinn had his up-to-date lesson in French swearwords, for the same driver swung alongside at the red light and started shouting insults at Gilles through his open window - in English.

Gilles wound his window down and let forth with a blast of ripe French swearwords and insults that sent the driver reeling back in his own car. The look of amazement on his shocked face had to be seen to be believed as he flinched under the stream of abuse hurled at his head by Gilles. Then Gilles wound his window up and charged off: 'See that? See that?' shouted Gilles. 'He thought I was a bloody Englishman.

Bet he never heard a bloody Englishman speak bloody French like that before.'

McGinn looked over his shoulder, fearful of hearing the familiar Wah-Wah of a police siren, but all he saw was angry-faced drivers striving to catch up. The hill leading from the two big supermarkets had become like the circuit of the Monte Carlo Grand Prix, with every driver trying to catch up with the GB lunatic who had carved them up.

Fortunately *Le Pirate* knew every back double in the town, and they shot through the maze of back streets and swung into an underground car park and came to a sudden halt.

'I don't suppose,' McGinn asked him, 'that you are in the pay of a Foreign Power to give the English a bad name on the French roads?'

Gilles laughed and said: 'No, but you think I could be a *cascadeur*?'

'A thousand times over.'

He seemed pleased. So pleased that he paid the parking fee.

On the way back from their shopping expedition he told McGinn that he had built his own cottage on a hill and carried every stone from the river bed 300 metres below, and that it had been a labour of love. When money ran out he went with his fiancée to the rubbish tips and found 'antiques', usually household contents and tools thrown out by a widow after a recent bereavement. Gilles' fiancée, however, was not enamoured with her new *'metier'*, standing in the hot sun of the flea market as sarcastic and truculent visitors examined the assortment of cracked tea-cups, chipped saucers, rusting *secateurs*, and the broken metal implements of bygone years.

She left him.

Outside his cottage was the tangled and mangled wreck of a yellow Citroen, looking as if it had turned over several times on the Giants' Causeway.

'The *cascadeurs'* training vehicle?' McGinn asked.

'That was the night she left me,' said Gilles sadly.

'You see, she was really too *bourgeois* for me. She couldn't stand the artists' life.'

Gilles had an outdoor toilet, too, but it was not as elegant as Pierre's. It was a wooden structure set a few inches off the ground, constructed by Gilles with low seating accommodation, up a pathway clustered with wild thyme and sage and heather. A well-hidden midden.

The view was magnificent.

'Once in Spain,' McGinn said to Gilles on his return, 'I took cheap lodgings in a farmhouse in the hills above Ronda, and when I asked the farmer for the toilet he opened the back door and there was a better view than this - all the way across the Sierra Nevada snow-capped mountain range. And he said: "Anywhere you like, Senor. Anywhere you like."'

Gilles looked wistful. Probably his happiest moments, after carrying stones to build a nest for his beautiful fiancée, were experienced crouched amongst the aromatic herbs on his wooden throne, communing with nature, seeing sunrise and sunset or just gazing into the distant hills.

'I have an idea,' he said. 'Raymond and Martine live in Mas Roland and Ginger is staying with them. They've rented the old schoolhouse, which has an apartment on top of it, and they have a view that is better than mine.'

They drove up the winding road to the tiny village. The schoolhouse garden was overgrown with weeds and blackberry bushes. There were two outhouses, one a sort of pavilion and the other a rough water closet. Once children had played here. On the other side of the road, in a little gully, was a row of stone-built houses. Although they were occupied they seemed sad. Houses sad? There was no doubt that there was a gloomy atmosphere. McGinn asked Martine about it when they had all exchanged greetings and been invited to stay for supper, and spend the night if it became too late to tackle the winding road back. The village died for two reasons: there were not enough children and the French State requires a minimum of eight pupils to keep a school open. But that was not the reason for the sadness of the village: young men had gone to two world wars from here and did not return. The fate of the tiny hamlet was decided on the battlefields of northern Europe in the first half of the century.

McGinn climbed the stairs of the schoolhouse and the view was indeed magnificent: the Mediterranean shimmered in a distant haze; the hills of Agde and Sète stood out against the glittering blue of the sea; to the right the snow-capped Pyrenees with the sun lighting up the peaks.

'Great view, eh?' said Raymond.

'A bit overdone, Bash,' McGinn said.

'I agree. I've complained to the Tourist Board about it, and they've agreed to try and tone the sunset down at weekends.'

They passed the afternoon and evening as many were passed in the Herault: with music and song; sausages, chops and *merguez* on the grill and lots of *pinard.* There was always the unforgettable flavour of food cooked on *sarments*, the pruned vine sticks which lay everywhere in abundance. Gilles played the harmonica, sounding like a full orchestra, and Ray and Ginger improvised with a tea-chest, broom handle and string, and an old washboard found in the outhouse, and played some old skiffle numbers. Young French couples came and went, politely shaking hands, trying a tune on a guitar. Some of them spoke *patois* or *langue d'oc*, the ancient language where 'yes' is *'oc'* as opposed to *'oïl'* which became the modern *'oui'* of the *langue d'oïl* which was spoken north of the Loire. It was the language of the lyric poets and troubadours of the 11th and 13th centuries. They wrote of chivalric love of women and the wandering life and heroic deeds of the great lords who protected them and who cultivated the art of the troubadour: the comtes de Toulouse, the Holy Roman Emperor, Friedrich Barbarossa, Alfonso II of Aragon, Richard the Lionheart, the marquis de Montferrat, and the comte de Foix.

Later someone suggested a seance: could they conjure up the ghost of a troubadour to recite and sing for them? The atmosphere of the place certainly lent itself to such thoughts.

Around a makeshift *'Oui-ja'* board they received scrambled 'messages' in mixed French and English and it ended in the usual squabbles of who pushed the glass and who didn't believe strongly enough in the seance.

Ginger, seeking privacy, elected to sleep in the ramshackle 'pavilion' in the garden. Gilles and McGinn camped near the log fire on mattresses and drifted into sleep in the aroma of burning *souches*, but McGinn was awakened at dawn by Gilles, restless and pensive, pitter-pattering back and forth in front of the dead fire, until McGinn groaned: 'Can't you sleep?'

'I am like a chicken, yes?' said Gilles, his droopy eye fluttering 'tick-tick-tick-and-tack-tack-tack.'

'Yes, Gilles. You are like a chicken. Now either lay an egg or go back to sleep.'

He went for a long country walk instead.

At breakfast, Ginger looked even more pensive and wound-up than Gilles. 'Something happened in the outhouse last night,' he said quietly. 'I thought I was dreaming. I was lying on that single narrow bed and I suddenly felt the presence of someone and saw a French soldier in the uniform of the First World War and he pushed me over on the mattress.'

'Too much red wine, Ginge,' said Raymond.

'No, Bash, I swear there was a French soldier there. You know me. I wouldn't invent something like this. It was that seance, I'm sure.'

Ray looked thoughtful: 'OK, Ginge, so what happened?'

'Nothing happened. There was just this presence and the dim figure of a young man in uniform pushing at my side, as if I were in his bed and he was politely shoving me out of it.'

Just then, Martine came into the kitchen carrying a vase of wild flowers, mainly poppies, that one of her girl friends had picked on a walk. She placed the vase on a table near the window.

'Who picked the poppies, Martine?' McGinn asked.

'Germaine. They're pretty, aren't they?'

'But don't you know that it's very bad luck to pick wild poppies? They're associated with the dead soldiers of Flanders Field in the First World War. The English never, ever pick poppies.'

'Superstition. They look nice and they can stay there.'

'I agree that it's superstition, but there's another older reason: wild poppies die so quickly. I'm surprised these are still alive. They won't last a day, even in water.'

The next day brought torrential rain, and with it the misery of a building site in a French village, with the trees dripping and gutters gushing and the unsmiling women in plastic macs waiting at the bread van, trying to squeeze under the canopy. Somehow the stones seem greyer as old men look at the sky, hoping and waiting, before they can re-enter the vineyards to work, and all the cats and dogs hiding indoors with the shutters pulled against the weather.

They had to *'crepi'* the newly-built wall where the huge doors of the barn had been, for McGinn had given the doors to a farmer in exchange for the use of his tractor, as the barter system and exchange of work system was still used in all the villages. It is a kind of fine pebble dash, with a mixture of rough sand, lime, cement and a touch of colouring if needed, and it is flung onto the new bricks as a protection, but it is not a job to do in the rain.

They entered the house like drowned rats when the job was completed, and someone suggested it was time to go to the shops to buy something for lunch. In France there is always that race against time to shop before the first stroke of twelve, for every door will be shut against you, and will remain closed for two to four hours depending on the region. Women can be seen dashing between butcher and baker and grocer looking at watches and shopping lists.

'The question is: which shop?' said Ginger.

'Your favourite, Ginge,' said Bash. 'Napoleon and Josefine.' There was laughter at this because that was one of the three shops within striking distance that Ginger did not enter, for the elderly shopkeepers, known to their customers as Napoleon and Josefine, bore him a lasting hatred for having beaten them at their own game: daylight robbery within the bounds of the Law.

'Is it a choice,' asked Dave, 'of sand in the sugar, water in the milk, or whisky in the jar?'

Ginger slapped Dave on the back. 'I'll go to Delmas, who is the fairest of the bunch, or Solange, or even bike over to the next village and go to the sausage specialists, but I do not enter the portals of Nap. and Jo, no sir.'

Each of these shops had a character of its own, and stories were exchanged about the shopkeepers and comparisons made of the various degrees of greed and profiteering that occurred in the price ring they all operated.

Dave's reference to whisky concerned Ginger going into Napoleon and Josefine's shop and being asked: 'Monsieur - do you drink English wine? We've got some English wine in stock but it's so old we can't sell it. It came with the stock from the previous owner.' Josefine showed him a sample bottle: the label read:: THE GLENLIVET.

'But this is Scotch whisky, not English wine,' said Ginger.

'It's been on that shelf for ten years, Monsieur. You can have it for five francs.' Ginger bought the bottle.

'Do you have any more?' he asked.

'Another eleven bottles in the cellar, Monsieur.'

Ginger bought the lot, and that year the *vendangeurs* were celebrating with whisky long after the harvest was over.

'Do you know they said she'd almost had a nervous breakdown when they found out the real price of Scotch,' said Ginger. 'They say Napoleon caught her as she fainted.'

The shop favoured by Ginger, Chez Delmas, was owned by a popular *vigneron* who always employed foreign grape pickers, housing them in the kind of accommodation which would have shocked Mother Teresa, but always showing great kindness to his workers. He had an unfortunate habit of using his deep freeze for purposes for which it was not intended, however, to the chagrin of his Irish porter on one occasion. The porter, Alfie, having lunched well on the three litres of wine he was allowed for his heavy work, rubbed his eyes with disbelief when he saw a squirrel in the shop's freezer.

'Will you look at that? A little squirrel,' he said, and addressed the *patron*: 'What's its name?' he asked.

'It doesn't have a name,' said Monsieur Delmas.

'Can I stroke it?' asked Alfie.

'If you wish,' said Monsieur Delmas.

'Isn't it a bit chilly in there for it? Surely it'll catch its death of cold,' said Alfie.

'It caught its death when I shot it at six o'clock this morning,' said Monsieur Delmas.

'Do you mean to say the poor little thing is dead?'

'Not only is it dead, but it's our supper tonight,' said the shopkeeper, to the great delight of his listening customers.

Ginger's reference to the sausage specialists referred to a husband-and-wife team who resembled Napoleon and Josefine in every respect except that when it came to pusillanimous behaviour, they were the champions.

Witnesses recounted how a small boy of seven asked for a kilo of sausages which were weighed and parcelled up by Madame herself, who then discovered the boy was five centimes short of the exact amount. She presented the problem to her husband, and he unwrapped the parcel and cut ten centimetres off one of the sausages and threw it back on the pile, giving the parcel back to his wife to re-wrap.

Other similar stories of avarice were told about Solange, next to the bread shop, many of them exaggerated: that she had a magnet under the scales, unwrapped chocolates in her apron pocket, and did her accounts by the light of the street lamp above the shop to save electric bills. One wag claimed that she had beheaded a jelly baby rather than over-weigh sweets for some schoolchildren.

'I suppose it's *cassoulet* again,' said Bash, 'the bachelor's favourite meal.'

There was a scratching at the door, then in came T.F. herself, thin and drenched, seeking friendly faces.

'And a tin of dogmeat for her,' said Bash to Ginger. 'She looks as if she hasn't eaten for a month.'

'Stale bread, that's all they get,' said Ginger, a dog-lover all his life. 'The job of a dog is to keep the vines clear of rabbits, and if it won't hunt it doesn't eat at all. And they go potty if you try and feed their cats. Their job is to keep down mice and rats in the barn and then to live off the little lizards in the fields.'

The heavy work on the house was due to finish that day, the roof insulated against the heat of summer with polystyrene and the tiles replaced, new windows and doors, bathroom, electric wiring and water heater in place in the wine cellar. Next it was the turn of the skilled French plasterers.

CHAPTER FOUR

TO WATCH a skilled French plasterer at work is fascinating and instructive, and the plasterer who came to work on McGinn's house, Jean-Paul, a shorter and skinnier version of the actor Jean-Paul Belmondo, was the champion of the whole district. His apprentice was a former French paratrooper called Patrice. Both worked in carpet slippers, which is usual in the trade. Patrice had new ones; J-P's were so old and worn they were attracting stray dogs.

The plaster they use comes from the mineral gypsum, or hydrated calcium sulphate, prepared from gypsums of Montmartre, Paris and hence the name Plaster of Paris, which adheres to the temperature of the body. It is flipped on to a wall like candle-wax; then. as it starts to set, forced on with a two-handled plaster board, then smoothed with a float. Finally the slimy residue in the bucket where the plasterer has washed his hands is kept and used for the finish, and an expert should be able to hit it with a hammer without denting it. The secret is not to touch it with the human hand but use only trowel and float.

McGinn held a saw to make the curves for a huge traditional chimney capable of taking metre-long logs, and J-P plastered the curves and finished the interior with split stone from Mas Roland and sixty heat-retaining fire bricks. This magnificent edifice supplied central heating for the cost of the logs, with the same water circulating through copper pipes.

When McGinn had first met Jean-Paul the plasterer, he was making supermarket ceilings by lying on his back on the scaffolding.

This kind of work is paid by the square metre, and consequently J-P would walk into the bar at the end of the week, and, with open-handed generosity, buy drinks for everyone in sight until the money was gone. There was no question of saving to pay rent, for he did not pay rent: he lived in a succession of old buses, caravans, *cabanons* or cabins in the vines, or, for a while, in a goat house which he had built for the goat-cheese maker. Two reasons for him leaving the goat house were given: the owner said he feared J-P's habit of smoking in bed might lead to the barbecuing of a herd of goats, but J-P claimed he had to leave because he was beginning to fancy the buck.

For a while he took up residence in a British Leyland bus belonging to a friend, Claudine, who had spent several weeks in Montpellier taking her Heavy Goods Vehicle course for a licence to drive the bus for purposes of tourism. She had bought it at a bargain price because it wouldn't start. She had specially ordered the new distributor head necessary to make it work, through the Paris agents for Leyland who were having to have it air-freighted to the South of France. By the time it arrived the bus was a burnt-out shell. It may have been parked on someone's land who objected to its presence or the sun's rays may have set fire to Jean-Paul's carpet slippers while he was in the local hostelry, but Claudine could be heard saying: 'Does anyone want to buy the distributor head for a British Leyland bus?'

His next residence was a *cabanon* in the vines which had a special attraction: it had water. Although it was not necessary for him to haul water in plastic drums as most residents of *cabanons* have to do, there was always the possibility of him stepping out of bed and falling seven metres into his well if he had forgotten to replace the lid the night before.

As water was plentiful in the deep well, his apprentice Patrice arrived with a full-size bath on the roof-rack of his car and placed it beneath the window on the outside of the *cabanon*. Although it was a bath with possibly one of the best views in the Languedoc, it was never used. Just as in certain Mediterranean countries it is believed that the exposure of the human body to the sun's rays, especially between November and March, is harmful to the skin, there is also a school of thought that the complete immersion of the body in water can be harmful, and J-P followed that rule except for the incident at Alignan-du-Vent.

This occurred towards the end of the grape harvest, when there were hundreds of Spanish workers in Roujan, the next village down the hill, almost doubling the population.

'I strongly advise you, Jean-Paul,' said his friend Josef, 'not to attempt to ride that Mobylette when you leave this bar.'

'Nonshensh,' said J-P, or words to that effect.

Josef and McGinn watched him mount the Mob. and zig-zag out of Alignan towards the steep hill that leads to Roujan.

'Come on, we'd better follow him,' said Josef and they jumped into his car and followed in the wake of the by now speeding Jean-Paul on the hill, his red tail-light waving about in the dark like an intoxicated glow-worm.

'Any minute now, he's going to fall off,' said Josef, and, sure enough, just as he reached the bottom of the hill it happened. Unfortunately he was alongside the deep ditch which, before they built the new and modern sewage works nearby, contained the effluvia and wastes of a village with twice its normal population, half of it being Spanish.

Mobylette and J-P went head first into the fetid miasma.

Luckily, Josef, himself in the building trade, happened to have a *'bâche'*, or builders' tarpaulin or canvas cover, in his boot, and he very sensibly used this to cover his back seat and wrap the plastered plasterer in the other half of it.

They say in Australia that you find your true friends when you are bitten on the backside by a red spider, a creature that has a nasty habit of hiding in toilet seats, and someone has to suck the poison out very quickly. Josef certainly proved his friendship by hauling J-P out of an open sewer and swaddling him in canvas until he was able to push him under a shower at his house in Alignan. Such friendship is rare in the building trade, especially in the French Midi, where competition is often fierce.

'I cannot understand,' McGinn said to J-P, 'Why Tom the plumber hasn't turned up with the radiators to finish the job.'

'Someone has stolen him away from you,' said J-P.

'Spider Smith?'

'More than likely.'

Spider Smith was certainly suspect number one, for he was a former *vendangeur* who knew every foreign building worker who was working 'black' in the area: i.e. paying no income tax or social security contribution, not insured against an industrial accident, drawing the French dole, and being paid weekly in cash, much to the annoyance of legitimate French builders who had a third of their wages deducted.

A narrow, winding street led up to the building Spider was working on, far too narrow for a truck or a car, so all his sand and cement and plaster was having to be wheelbarrowed in from the village square where it had been dumped. The front door was open. Inside, in the basement, was a toilet which looked more like a throne.

This indicated that the premises Spider had bought were formerly used by the grape pickers, for the *patron* put the toilet in as cheaply and as close to the main sewage system as possible, always in the basement, and often just inside the front door, with scant regard for the niceties of interior design or decor, or privacy.

'Wot brings you 'ere, then?' asked Spider on the stairs, with his heavy Devon burr. 'Lookin' for a job? I'm in need of an extra man.'

'I'm looking for Tom plumb.'

'Arr - so am I. We might be lucky if we see 'im before Christmas. I give 'im 'is deposit for the job. This mornin' 'e turned up and left 'is blow-lamp and a hammer then orf 'e went. Why do you want 'im?'

'He's supposed to finish my central heating.'

'Central 'eatin'? You're a bit posh, aren't yer? Anyway, you won't be needin' that this side of November. Shouldn't be surprised if Tom went orf on 'is 'olidays. That's 'im, init? Leaves 'is bleedin' paint-pot inside the door and buggers off on 'is alcoholidays. One thing's sure - you won't find 'im in the public library studyin'.'

'How's the work going, anyway?'

'Not bad. Champagne Jock turned up 'ere for work this mornin' with the rest of the gang, then 'e jacked after ten minutes. We're layin' a cement floor up there an' we all got stuck into the mix, heavin' sand into the mixer, and after ten minutes Jock said: "Stop. Stop. We canna have this. Ah'm off." So wot's wrong with you, Jock? says I. "Ah'm jackin' that's what," says Jock. Why, what's the matter? I asked 'im. "Ah'm beginnin' to sweat, that's what," says he. "Ah canna have that," an' orf 'e goes down the street. So I'm lookin' for an extra man.'

'Well don't look at me.'

'That Jock must have plenty of money. 'e turned down jobs in Rotterdam, too, before 'e come down 'ere. I offered to get 'im a start laggin' the ships' boilers. Dirty work but three hundred notes a week, like, but 'e said no to that.'

The Scotsman's source of income was a total mystery. He acquired his nickname because he was in the habit of giving champagne parties every so often, inviting everyone back to his house, where his French wife, Brigitte, would cook excellent casseroles and Jock would dispense champagne. He appeared to be some kind of agent for luggage, for he often tried to sell leather or canvas suitcases to his friends or visitors to the champagne parties, at a good discount, often forty percent off the shop price.

'If you know anyone who wants to get on the mixer, send 'im over,' said Spider.

At this moment the shutters of the house opposite opened and an elderly lady shook her fist at Spider and called out to him angrily that as soon as she was in better health she was going to see her solicitor about him.

'Oh, ta gueule, Madame,' Spider shouted back at her.

'She's always goin' on about the noise,' said Spider, 'every time we start up the mixer she's yellin' at me. I don't understand her anyway, so what's the use.' Even after many grape harvests, Spider's French was limited to ordering drinks in the bar, food in a restaurant, and a few swear words and insults, like *'ta gueule'* or 'shut up'.

The shutters were scrunched and banged shut with that same awful finality, and Spider glared at them, his face bright red from a mixture of embarrassment, sunshine and wine.

'Come an' look, anyway. I've fallen on my feet 'ere, I 'ave,' said Spider. 'See what I've got for my money.'

The house was indeed enormous, as some village houses are in the Midi, often with rooms leading on to caves and storerooms, sometimes honeycombed into a hillside, and Spider, having sent his work-team to the café for a break, proudly gave a conducted tour of his cellars and lofts.

'If you asked me the price of it, I wouldn't tell you, as you know, 'cos only half is declared to the State and the other half is paid "under the table" so everybody keeps schtum about house prices, but if I was to say I got these premises for the price of a small Italian car with black wall tyres and no radio, that'd be about right. Not only that - I got two gaffs for the price of one because there's a little house adjoining this one called "bis". It means half or somethin' like that. Like this is number twenty three and then there's twenty three "bis", and I'm going to do that second house up when I've tarted this one up.'

'I think it means twice or second or double,' said McGinn, 'and they use it sometimes if they're superstitious about number thirteen, so you get twelve and twelve *bis* in a street.'

'What I'm goin' to do is let this one to tourists and live in "bis" next door. But I've got to get Tom to move that there crapper up a floor 'cos the tourists won't like squattin' there, three feet off the ground with their strides an' keks danglin' in the dust.'

'Tom's taken a deposit on my job as well.'

'He has to, I suppose. Most of the time he never gets paid the second half so he has to sue 'em and it takes two to three years to get the spondulix out of 'em. And it's most often the Brits who stiff 'im. But 'e doesn't let mates down. Don't worry, he'll be back. He was a bit upset this morning. His missus is choked because he's resigned from Alcoholics Anonymous. He said he couldn't stand the pace. All they did was look at their watches then hurl down large scotches at the end of the meetin'.'

'So why was he upset?'

'Well, she said to him: "If you're goin' to kill yourself, would you try an' do it in the car - that way I'm insured." Look out! STAY OUT OF SIGHT!' Spider dragged McGinn back from the window overlooking the street. A weather-beaten *viticulteur* strode purposefully towards number twenty three. At the open door he started shouting for *Monsieur Smith.*

'Tell 'im I'm in the café with the lads,' whispered Spider in my ear.

When the farmer had disappeared up the street towards the café, Spider said: 'I've got myself into a right load of bother with 'im. He claims I owe him a grand. And I mean Sterling. Ten thousand *francs,* not *centimes.* Lost in a card game. I thought he was joking when he said he wanted to play one game for a brick. He said *brique* like in French an' I thought he meant a brick as in buildin' site brick. 'Ow was I to know it's French slang for ten thousand francs? He'd already won practically everything off me anyway, so I thought he was being friendly. Now 'e's trying to collect. Come on, let's get out of 'ere before he comes back with 'is shotgun. I'm goin' to look for Tom, and I won't be touring the churches and the cake shops, either.'

Accompanying Spider to his car, with him keeping a weather eye out for the farmer, McGinn noticed his Citroen with the Dutch number plates had taken a hammering since last he had seen it. New dents had appeared on each corner.

'Yes, I know, but not to worry,' said Spider, 'I got this French car for a burnt match in Amsterdam. The Dutch get a new car every year and they give bangers away. That,' he continued, pointing at a smashed headlight, 'was your mate the plasterer in Alignan. Give 'im a lift when 'e was Molly the Monk. Turn left, sez 'e - an' bang, straight into a bollard we didn't know was there. That,' he pointed at a dented fender, 'was the Fête at Margon. And that there tail light was done by some Jodrell Banker who 'it me roight up the arse at the Pézenas lights. And,' he added, pointing down the small hill that led from the square to the main road, 'if they don't move that bloody church, I'll have no bloody car left.'

What he said was true, for the hill had not been built to accommodate cars, and only skilful drivers managed to negotiate the curve without chipping away a little piece of history. Deep gashes were cut into the main pillar.

'Some day the whole bloody portico is goin' to collapse if people keep hitting it,' said Spider, starting up.

'You know how they have those stickers in cars for visitors to Lowestoft, Margate, and resorts in England? McGinn said. 'They could have them here for dents in cars: *Fête de Margon; l'Eglise à Neffies; Alignan-du-Vent, le bollard,* etcetera.'

Spider chuckled: 'If I wanted to get rich in France there's one business where you'll always make a fortune.'

'What's that?'

'Panel beatin',' he said, laughing so much his red cheeks wobbled.

'The French are realists, Spider,' McGinn said. 'They *expect* people to dent cars. We pretend to be shocked when it happens. That's why they call a dodgem car an *auto tamponneuse* - a car for bashing into another. Where would the fun be if you managed to dodge each time and never actually hit another car, making the girls shriek with laughter?'

'Talkin' about dodgems...' Spider had been glancing in his rear-view mirror and had seen a distant figure emerge from the bar. 'I'm off, here comes Minnesota Fats himself. If you can't beat 'em - dodge 'em.'

McGinn watched him try and negotiate the church corner on the hill in the Citroen which must have once had a proud Dutch owner, and heard the s-c-r-u-n-c-h as modern chrome fender took another slice of ancient Arles stone out of the pillar, and Spider gave a small toot of farewell as he headed downhill and away from the card player who had now broken into a run.

When McGinn returned to his own building site which by now had some semblance of habitable accommodation as opposed to the rubble-filled adventure playground for commandos that Spider's house resembled, he saw from Patrice's face that all was not well.

'Marie-Lise has been here,' he said, in the kind of tremulous voice he would have used to announce: 'The Gestapo have just called.'

'Marie-Lise?'

'The wife of Jean-Paul. All the way from Normandy. She took him away.'

'That little thing? She's no bigger than a flea.'

'He is afraid of her. She is looking for money. His *cabanon* has been broken into, the lock smashed, the mattress cut.'

'I don't suppose she went down the well?'

Patrice looked puzzled. 'Why?'

'Don't you see - it's even better that the file-in-the-cake idea. We spread the rumour so that it gets to her ears that J-P's money is hidden in the well. She'll go down there in frogman's gear looking for it.'

'Somehow,' said Patrice with a grin, 'I don't think she will ever try subterranean exploration again.'

That was the way Jean-Paul had met his wife-to-be, on a cave-exploring expedition with Francois the Fingers, an expert speleologist and three-finger amputee who had learnt his skill with Michel Siffre, a true troglodyte who would eschew wives, girl-friends and the whole human race by spending several months in caverns in the Alpes Maritimes. It was Francois the Fingers who had invited Jean-Paul to join him and his then fiancée Marie-Lise down the hole.

Throughout the expedition she insulted, abused and nagged Francois until he said to Jean-Paul: 'I know a good restaurant ten kilometres from here where we can have lunch.'

On the way to the restaurant, with Francois humming a tune as he drove, Jean-Paul asked him: 'Haven't we forgotten something?'

'Like what?' Francois asked.

'Like your girlfriend, Marie-Lise.'

'It's OK. She'll be there when we get back,' said Francois, having left her down a 60 foot hole when he pulled up the cord.

Not only was she there two hours later but she was still hurling abuse at Francois through the aperture. It was this persistence, determination and fierce Norman independence which attracted Jean-Paul to her, and six months later they were married. Francois the Fingers gave him a rope ladder, a fishing rod, and a pair of ear-plugs as wedding presents.

Jean-Paul had soon tired of building the family mansion on the cold coast of Normandy, however, and would frequently make a dash for freedom and a beaker of the warm South.

'It's OK, I can finish off the plastering,' said Patrice.

'Wives and families,' McGinn said.

'What's that? Pardon?'

'This place is supposed to be ready and fit for human habitation when Carolyn and her son Rupert come down at the end of the month. We haven't even started on his room yet, and her workroom must be ready for sewing and knitting machines and paraphernalia for when her dress shop opens in Pézenas.'

'Stop worrying. I'll do the tiling and the plastering in the boy's room and you can paint the walls and door in Madam's workroom and it will be all finished when they arrive.'

'But you're only learning plastering.'

'I know enough to do this work. Don't worry any more about it. I know the tourist season is starting soon - in fact here it has started. I heard German voices outside today. Either the Danish painter or the American-German photographer is letting a house to visitors.'

McGinn was not sure how to take this news: the first tourists in the village, which, he had been told when he bought the property was *'une village perdu'*. Surely it hadn't been discovered already?

In the street outside, Monsieur Marcel his neighbour was carefully urinating against an elm tree outside his front door. This grizzled septuagenarian grape grower would surely know if there were visitors to the village.

'O,' he said when he had adjusted his dress. This meant in English:

'Good day, how are you?' His *patois* was fluent and almost unintelligible. McGinn asked him about the German tourists. Was it true?

'*La haut,*' he said, pointing to the top of the village where the church was. 'Up there' could have meant anyone, but McGinn strolled up out of curiosity and there, sure enough were two strangers in the camp.

'Hello, do you speak English?' a chirpy voice called from a terrace which overlooked the vines and the hills. Inge and her friend George invited McGinn to join them for a drink. 'So you are building a house here?' Inge asked, and he talked houses and house prices and the cost of material and electricians and plumbers for a while until Inge asked:

'Who is that dirty old man who lives below here?'

Who on earth could she mean? McGinn would not have attached such a description to any of his new-found friends or neighbours in the village.

'Which one?'

'The one with the watering can,' said Inge.

He tried to think who the keen gardeners were. There were not many. Their gardens, if they existed at all, were postage-stamp sized patches in the corners of vineyards, usually with a well and diesel pump, for water lay five to seven metres down in most flat parts of the Herault.

'A gardener, do you mean?'

'No, he doesn't use it for gardening. He washes his bum with it. Every morning I see him go down into the vines with his watering can and do his business and then wash himself with water. It's really horrible.'

This was news to McGinn, for he did not have the same panoramic view from his terrace; but how to explain to Inge from a high-rise in Berlin that expecting a true French *paysan* or peasant to buy scented toilet rolls was like expecting an Australian Aborigine to invest in Kleenex tissues? Again, would she appreciate being told that she should feel privileged to have witnessed an ancient and recondite ritual performed by Monsieur Marcel, surely the last of a dying breed, in the privacy of his own fertile vineyard?

'It's a countryman's custom,' McGinn said. 'And besides, there's his wife, daughter, Aunt, son-in-law and three grandchildren sharing his house. Perhaps there's a run on the bathroom in the mornings.'

'Maybe, but it spoils my breakfast. It's really horrible. Next year we will go to Africa.'

'But they do it in the river there in case the witch doctor gets hold of a piece and casts a spell on them.'

'You are joking me.'

'Not at all.'

'That doesn't concern us, anyway, as we only go to Neckermann recommended hotels. So goodbye, then and hope your house goes well. Now it is time for the beach. Do you go swimming?'

'Not in the Mediterranean.'

'Oh, why?'

'Well, if you walk along a beach and see someone motionless, paddling a little, in the sea, you can imagine what they're doing. You can tell because they always have a little smile on their face. Bye-bye.'

As he walked downhill he heard Inge's piercing voice addressing George: 'Do you think he can be serious? Is it English humour as they call it?'

'Let's go, Patrice,' McGinn said, 'It's *apéritif* time.'

'Where?' he asked as he washed the plaster off his hands.

'The fireman's bar in the next village. You never know, we may be lucky.'

They drove in Patrice's Deux Chevaux to the bar in a nearby village which McGinn had come to call the Firemen's Bar, for it was rented from the restaurant owner, whose premises were above the bar, by two brothers who either fought fires in their spare time or ran the bar in their spare time. The bar was really doomed to failure. Firemen, like Gendarmes in France often take part-time work, mainly in security firms, to supplement their incomes, but unfortunately the busy time for bars in the South of France coincides with the busy time for fires: i.e. the height of the summer. In winter, when the brothers really did have spare time, there were few customers in the bar.

Firemen throughout the world have time on their hands, and, like sailors and long-term prisoners, are often well-read and occasionally become very competent writers. Rather than follow in the footsteps of the Goncourt brothers, however, and devote their hours to the literary life, the *sapeurs-pompiers* unwisely chose the bar trade.

A red getaway car stood at the entrance to the café-bar. This was for emergencies. It was the property of the local Fire Brigade and was kept tanked up with petrol and always ready for a mad dash into the *garrigue* to beat out flames.

One of the brothers, the married one, was behind the bar when they entered, looking rather furtive and a trifle suspicious.

'He must have been stock-taking,' McGinn said to Patrice.

Patrice snuffled into his anorak and ordered two Ricards, the fireman giving suspicious glances throughout the pouring and watering operation. McGinn may have been mistaken, but he had the impression that he was totally paranoid.

He had the feeling that if the fire bell which had been specially installed in the bar to call the brothers to action had suddenly gone off, he would have jumped three feet in the air.

The brothers had good reason to be nervous: McGinn had been in the bar with a dozen or more customers, mainly local men, when the bell had gone off. Leaping into action the *sapeur-pompier* behind the jump threw the keys of the till and the door to a customer he knew and (presumably) trusted, and hurtled out through the door and leaped into the red fire car to scream off in pursuit of the engine.

This was a signal for the customers to celebrate another fire by helping themselves liberally to drinks during the bartender's absence. The 'trusty' would go behind the bar and to cries of *'Allez'*, and *'un autre'* and a forest of thrusting hands holding empty glasses, would start a race to see how many drinks could be downed before the flames were quenched in the hills.

'His wife is furious,' said Patrice in a hoarse whisper, just out of earshot of the twitching server. 'She can't understand why there are so many empty bottles and so few francs in the till.'

'I hear she tried to sell someone a ticket for the Fireman's Ball,' McGinn whispered back, 'and when they said they didn't dance, she said it wasn't a dance - it was a raffle.'

After several seconds thought, Patrice exploded into laughter and the barman twitched again and glared at them with such fury that they decided to take their drinks out onto the terrace.

'We shouldn't really laugh,' McGinn said. 'The poor fellow is suffering from paranoia. His nerves are shot.'

'Sounds just like Jean-Paul,' said Patrice, 'this business with Marie-Lise has got him so nervous and paranoid that when he found himself walking back to his *cabanon* with two elderly ladies in front of him, he

Peter Kinsley

went and hid in the vines in case they reported him for following them.'

'I'm getting that way myself. I'm beginning to suspect that the lady on the bread van, and even the ones in the bread shops, give me the *"pain recuperer"*, the old bread warmed up, because I'm a single man and a foreigner.'

'That's not paranoia,' said Patrice. 'They do that here. Village women wouldn't accept it but we have to. You have to be married here to get fresh bread. But don't protest too much. If the baker wants to give you bad luck he places the *flute* or *baguette* upside down for you. That's what they did to show which loaf was for the *bourreau*, the hangman in the old days. Never, ever give someone their bread face down.'

'I'll try and remember that.'

'They tried that on the Sheriff in my village and he threatened to pull his gun on them.'

'The Sheriff?'

'Oh, you haven't made his acquaintance yet? He's the new policeman on traffic duty at the crossroads: about as tall as a sack of flour and as pale, bullying motorists all day long. He's friendly with me because I buy him drinks. Calls me by my first name. Best to keep in with him because from where he stands he can almost count how many drinks I have had before I drive off. Let's go on to my village for a drink and you can see him in operation. This bar is making me nervous. If that fire bell went off now he'd probably tie us up and gag us until he'd put the fire out.'

The Sheriff was in action when we arrived. He straddled the highway, arms akimbo, whistle in mouth, gun slung low and swinging ever so slightly in the holster. The municipality had put their officer on duty at the crossroads as it had become an accident black spot. Perhaps because it would interfere with the joys of motoring, they adamantly refused to erect a 'Go Slow' or 'Reduce Speed' or '40 km' sign at the entrance to the village. As a concession to the school they had painted red stripes on two zebra crossings as a warning, but old ladies sauntering across the main road in their dressing gowns to buy bread would leap to the sough of giant airbrakes on a huge truck or to the scream of brakes applied by a Porsche driver as he got them in his sights. The old ladies would screech curses at the 20th century driver who would hurl abuse and his opinion of 19th century mentality pedestrians.

That was until the Sheriff arrived.

The very sight of his stocky little figure would slow drivers down as they came in sight of him. Appeased by their look of wariness or fear, he would wave them on. Anyone not slowing down would get the whistle. Then the Sheriff would slowly swagger over to them, gun swinging low, and yell: *'papiers'* through the open window at the driver.

The fight with the bread shop was over the tiny parking facility just outside the doorway. As the French hate to walk more than five yards from the car unless it is absolutely necessary, everyone seeking bread tried to park in the space allotted, which was not quite big enough for a large car. Each car that stopped heard the Sheriff's whistle and saw him wave them away from the front of the shop.

'He's losing them business,' said Patrice when they had settled on the Grand Café terrace. 'If he makes them move they don't park nearby - they go to the other bread shop.'

'So they gave him the *"bourreau's"* bread, the hangman's loaf?'

'Right. He can get very angry. I thought he would burst a blood vessel last week. Some British tourists got the whistle for speeding and when he shouted *"papiers"*, the driver gave him the toilet roll out of the glove compartment - must have thought he wanted to go to the lavatory. I went over and explained that the British don't have identity cards or "papers" and it was a language mix-up and not an insult. Here he comes now.'

The Sheriff came over to the café, taking advantage of a lull in the traffic during the midday break.

'Salut, Patrice,' he called, and Patrice signalled with thumb to mouth, asking if he wanted a drink.

'Un café,' the Sheriff called and went inside out of sight. With another hand signal Patrice indicated to the *patronne* that the Sheriff's coffee was on his tab. 'Notice he takes his *képi* off when he gets to the terrace,' said Patrice, 'and that means he's off-duty.'

'You mean I can hit him?'

Patrice laughed. 'It means that for the next ten minutes he will attempt to play the rôle of a human being, discussing the weather, accepting drinks, trying to be one of the boys. But as soon as he puts that *képi* back on - watch out.'

'By the way - what do I need to get in Pézenas this afternoon?'

'For the moment, three sacks of plaster and one sponge. I'm doing the bedroom wall the easy way. There's two ways of plastering, *"lisse"*, the way Jean-Paul does it, meaning flat and smooth, or *"rustique"* - finished with a sponge, and that's the easy way.'

During the afternoon, on the way to the builders' yard on the outskirts of the town, McGinn was hailed by Henry Catchpole, a Londoner who had bought and was restoring an old farmhouse near the town. He claimed to come from a long line of costermongers and that his Cockney ancestors were mentioned in the works of Charles Dickens. He sold what he called 'schmutter' from a stall in the market, having access to the previous year's fashions from the Katherine Hamnet fashion house in London on the strict understanding that he remove the labels and traded only in South West France.

Sitting with him were two English ladies from the Home Counties who had also bought property in the town, Miss Angela and Miss Elizabeth, who had tried for many years, and failed, to have the Spanish Government ban bullfighting and were now campaigning for a ban on *foie gras* and the cruel force-feeding of ducks and geese to enlarge their livers for the market, and a ban on horse-butchering throughout France. They were members of the Royal Society for the Prevention of Cruelty to Animals and the Royal Society for the Protection of Birds. Miss Elizabeth was the stout, horsey, tweedy one, and Miss Angela, skinny and rather Bohemian in dress, could have been gainfully employed as a scarecrow in any farmer's field. Although the exact nature of their sexual proclivities remained a mystery, they would have been known, in the world of the London theatre, as Diesel and Spook, Miss Elizabeth being the diesel and Miss Angela the spook.

'Do you want a kitten?' Henry asked as McGinn joined them.

'Please do give him a home,' said Miss Angela. 'He's very sweet and we rescued him from certain starvation.'

'Aren't your family comin' aht soon?' Henry asked. 'How old is the boy?'

'Rupert will be eight in June. I'd have liked to get a dog, but the British quarantine laws make it impossible because every time you go back to England you have to foist the dog onto someone. There's an idea for you Miss Elizabeth - looking after dogs while the owners are in the UK.'

'Distemper,' said Miss Elizabeth. 'Very hard to control. If one animal gets it they all get it. Much better to have a cat in that case. Wonderful animals. Fend for themselves in an emergency, field mice, lizards, y'know.'

'All right, I'll take the kitten. Has it got a name?'

'*Mouche*. He's very good at catching flies. We'll deliver him to you in our cat basket. Mr Catchpole has explained where you live. You won't be disappointed. He has a tremendous character.'

They stood up and gathered their belongings and their shopping together, then sauntered off through the town followed by the curious stares of the local people.

'Didn't mean to lumber you,' said Henry.

'No, it's OK. Rupert loves animals. How's business, anyway?'

'How's business? I once did a *vendange* with Ingray, and he knew a film director called Maskiewicz or something like that, who'd made a film called *Midnight in Vienna*. One rainy night 'e was drivin' through Nottingham and saw the film on at a local cinema. He stopped and asked the feller in the box office: "How's business?" and this feller said: "It's about the same as if you was showin' *Midnight in Nottingham* in Vienna, mate." They don't believe the schmutter is genuine. They either say, "Fell orf the back of a lorry, did it?" or they say I'm lyin' abaht the labels I cut aht. Can't win. Anyway, I'm cornerin' the market in *comports*. Got a few garden centres in England interested: "French oak wine bins", I call 'em. Pay forty francs and sell 'em for fourteen quid, two vanloads I can make a fahsand pahnd. Which reminds me, Francois has got two dozen for me to pick up.'

'Francois the Fingers?'

'Nah - Francois the Froat.'

Henry Catchpole had a tendency to christen French acquaintances according to their characteristics or foibles. Francois the froat talked with a growl, the result of an operation on his vocal chords.

'I fink 'e gets 'em for nuffink - or twenty francs at most, so I'm supplementin' 'is pension payin' forty bollocks.'

They were interrupted by the arrival of Pierre the farmer, and when Henry Catchpole had taken his leave, Pierre said: 'The asparagus is ready.'

'The asparagus?'

'Remember? Ben Aissa's field of asparagus. I'm going up there tonight, and I need a lookout. There's no moon tonight, so it's perfect. We can fill the *congelateur*. Will you keep a lookout for me?'

'If there's no moon, why do you need a lookout?'

'Because Aissa's on guard with a 12-bore shotgun.'

'Is his *patronne* paying overtime?'

'Do pigs fly?'

'But he knows.'

'Sure, it's all arranged. He'll be guarding one end of the field while I'm at the other end with the asparagus knife. You wait in my car and give one toot on the klaxon if you see a car or *les flics* approaching. You then get out and open the boot and the hood and I run back and pretend we've broken down. Aissa must see nothing, then he can truthfully say to his *patronne* that he saw no-one.'

'OK. What time and where?'

'By the way - do you like asparagus warm with butter, or cold with mayonnaise?'

Pierre was already planning Sunday's menu.

'Either way will do. The only thing I don't like is *bouillie*, what the English call porridge. It's what you get in prison.'

'Not French prison. Stop worrying. Everything will be all right, but not a word to Siddo. She thinks I'm getting it from a farmer for repairing his tractor.'

Pierre convinced McGinn that the operation was a kind of Robin Hood exercise on behalf of the Arab workforce who were being cheated out of their overtime by a mean *patronne*. The field of asparagus lay in total darkness off the road which mounted to a bridge where Pierre parked the car after they had met at the café that night. In the deceptive darkness McGinn thought he saw a quick glow of a cigarette at the far end of the field.

'He's there. He heard the car. Don't worry, he won't shoot. If he did his *patronne* would deduct the cost of the cartridges from his pay.' He took two shallow fruit boxes from the boot of the car and disappeared down the embankment with a pencil torch and a long asparagus knife. From time to time, McGinn saw the pinpoint of light moving in the field, like a glow-worm flitting from plant to plant.

Suddenly there was the sound of a car and its lights shone in the rear-view mirror. McGinn jumped out and flung open the boot and then the hood, as instructed by Pierre, then realised that he had forgotten to signal to him by sounding the horn. The other car stopped and the driver walked back and said: 'Run out of gas?'

'No. Can't seem to find the trouble.'

'I'll get a light,' he said and returned with a torch. McGinn imagined Pierre lying low in the field and cursing him for not signalling.

'You try and start the motor while I take a look,' said the helpful stranger, flashing his torch into the open hood.

The only way to get rid of him was to start the car, and when McGinn did so, he slammed the hood down and came up to the driver's window. 'Seems to be all right now,' he said.

'Maybe overheating or something,' McGinn mumbled. 'Thanks for your help, Monsieur. Very kind of you.'

'You're welcome,' he called, and waved his hand and drove off.

Pierre appeared out of the darkness: 'Why didn't you klaxon?' he asked.

'Forgot, sorry,' McGinn said.

'If that had been *les flics* we'd have been on our way to jail now.'

'You. Not me,' McGinn said. 'Anyway, you're mad risking being caught for a few sticks of asparagus.'

He went down the bankside and returned heaving the two boxes with him; they were filled to overflowing with choice asparagus. 'What do you mean, "a few sticks"? Do you know how much stuff like this costs per kilo? The only pity is that I won't see the *patronne's* face as she searches the field wondering why nothing has sprouted yet. She's got a twenty four hours a day guard - Aissa and his pals - on this field and she hasn't had a taste of the asparagus so far.'

'Can we go now?'

'Yes, let's go. This asparagus will taste great on Sunday, just you wait and see. Revenge is sweet, as they say.'

The parsimonious *patronne* never did solve the mystery of the disappearing asparagus. She had planted roots which would mature in two years and drawn a blank, but she must have had her suspicions, for the field was ploughed over and vines on wires planted after that, and the luscious sticks at Pierre's farm on Sundays were as good as he had promised: hot with melted butter or cold with mayonnaise or *vinaigrette*.

On the day that Miss Angela and Miss Elizabeth were due to deliver Mouche the kitten, McGinn heard a tremendous commotion in the village street. Angry voices were being raised, and the voices were English: 'This dog is hungry - just look at the poor thing. Haven't you read the notice in the *Mairie*: you are no longer living in the eighteenth century, stop the cruelty to animals. Can't you read?'

'Parle Francais,' T.F.'s owner was shouting back at them. It appeared that Miss Angela and Miss Elizabeth had tried to dog-nap *Toujours Faim* from the rightful owner and had been caught in the act.

'You ought to be horse-whipped,' Miss Elizabeth shouted. 'You don't feed your dogs properly and you don't walk your dogs. Look at this street. It's a disgrace. Can't you exercise your dogs like civilised people?'

'We'll report you for cruelty,' piped Miss Angela.

'Miss Angela, Miss Elizabeth,' McGinn called. 'Have you got my kitten?'

The interruption gave T.F.'s owner the chance he was waiting for. He pulled his dog from Miss Elizabeth and ran into his house and slammed the door.

They came towards McGinn, still shouting angrily.

'They're too damned lazy to walk a dog a few yards down into the fields. They just let them do their business on the damned doorstep. Flies and disease, that's what it causes,' shouted Miss Elizabeth.

'The poor doggies are prisoners all their lives,' said Miss Angela. She broke away to go to their car and fetch the cane basket which contained the kitten.

'No, we won't come in. I'm too angry for words,' said Miss Elizabeth.

'The dogs in cages are hunting dogs,' McGinn said, *'chien de sanglier*, kept for wild boar hunting.'

'Agreed,' said Miss Elizabeth, 'but they keep their other dogs caged up, the ones they breed to sell. The poor things never get any exercise at all. Even men in jail are allowed to take exercise.'

'Anyway,' said Miss Angela, 'here's the kitten. I'm sure you'll give him a good home. Sorry to make a fuss in your village but we get so angry when we see anyone being unkind to animals, and they *have* put up notices in all these villages about it.'

They refused to accept the offer of tea, and drove off, still fuming.

The hour of *apéritif* drew the usual crowd in the town and Pierre was joined by Aissa and one of his Moroccan worker friends who said he wanted to ask McGinn to do him a favour. Aissa told McGinn his friend wanted to buy a pair of spectacles, and McGinn couldn't understand why he didn't go to an optician until Aissa produced an advertisement from a magazine. It showed a man wearing square glasses and looking at a drawing of a woman which showed the outline of her legs and underwear.

The advertisement was probably aimed at naughty schoolboys and claimed that the 'magic' spectacles enabled the wearer to see through women's dresses. McGinn told Aissa that he absolutely refused to let his friend waste his hard-earned money on what amounted to a confidence trick, but his friend seemed disappointed, and even shocked at Pierre's suggestion that if he wanted to know what women looked like under their dresses he should have a sniff around the beaches in summer.

There was a lull in the conversation, and everyone thought about summer which was just around the corner, when the town which was now empty would fill with holiday visitors. Aissa scratched his Brillo-pad hair under his woollen hat; his friend, faced with the prospect of having to rely on his imagination, being unable, through illiteracy, to apply for the 'magic specs' himself, sadly put the magazine in his pocket; Pierre looked thoughtful, then suddenly brightened:

'C'est le marché demain,' he said.

Of course, market day on Saturday: life was not as dull as it seemed, after all, and tomorrow there would be men selling chickens and ducks and young turkeys and pigeons, and women selling olives from every country in the Mediterranean, large olives and small, green and black, stuffed with almonds and anchovies and red peppers, and a cheese stall with Camembert and Brie from Normandy, Roquefort from the Aveyron, black-skinned Pyrenees, and all the goat cheeses and Cantal, and the *bleu be Bresse, blue de Causses* and *bleu d'Auvergne* and country butter in big slabs...

Market day, the highlight of the week in any French town or village, dawned bright and sunny, and the municipal police went around with half a dozen stallholders in their wake and allotted any vacancies in the much sought-after spaces that had not been filled by 7 a.m. As there were rarely more than one or two vacant spaces, the disappointed stallholders would have to wait until afternoon when someone packed up and went home.

On the terrace of the café, Martine joined the small group who had begun to make a ritual out of buying fresh food and pâté and charcuterie and cheese in the market and having a picnic on the terrace. This was accepted by most bar owners in the region so long as the customers bought drinks: some, if they knew you, provided salt, pepper, mustard, plates and cutlery, and even paid a round of drinks at the end of the meal.

'The poppies are still alive after three weeks,' said Martine. Ginger and McGinn exchanged glances.

'It's not possible,' said Ginger.

'I've never in my life known poppies to live longer than a couple of days once they're picked,' McGinn said. 'You're not making it up, are you?'

'No, it's true. Of course I change the water. It must be the altitude that keeps them alive so long.'

'You know, maybe something happened in that séance that we can't understand,' said Ginger. 'It was a weird experience, that's sure, with that French soldier trying to push me out of bed.'

They thought about it, and suddenly Martine shivered, and a cloud passed briefly over the sun and the brightness of the market day faded. She stood up and took a woollen jumper from her basket.

The spell was broken by the hasty arrival of Henry Catchpole, who came running from the end of the market where they sold the livestock, near the municipal park that contained the war memorial.

''ere - come an' look at this, you lot. This you gotta see. Talk abaht bleedin' eccentrics. It's Gert and Daisy - they're releasin' all the bleedin' cage birds.'

They hurried after Henry to where a little man in a black beret was shouting at Miss Elizabeth and Miss Angela, who had caused chaos in the market by opening a bird cage and releasing their brightly coloured friends into the freedom of the streets. Small boys were running after them jumping up to ledges where the newly-released linnets and goldfinches and a variety of song-birds were settling, just out of snatching distance.

'The kids are tryin' to capture 'em cos they're werf abaht a tenner each,' said Henry Catchpole, appalled by this loss of profit which would have shocked his long line of costermongering forbears. 'The silly old moos are frowin' away a forchin.'

'We've bought them and we'll do as we wish with them,' called Miss Elizabeth to the assembled curious throng.

'Fly away my pretty ones. Freedom is yours,' cried Miss Angela, waving her arms in the air.

'Do you know these people eat *robins*?' said Miss Elizabeth in her best Home Counties horsey voice.

'It sets the whole world in a rage,
    A robin redbreast in a cage...'

quoted Miss Angela, looking sternly at the little stallkeeper, who suddenly snapped shut his gaping mouth and let loose with a stream of heavily accented Catalan and French.

Champagne Jock arrived on the scene with his French wife Brigitte, and asked: 'What's going on here?' and Brigitte asked the stallholder what his problem was.

''Ee says, zat you mus' throw zem away in ze *campagne*, in ze wild country, an' next week you mus' buy ze cage as well an' take it wiz you. Not to throw zem away in ze town, where ze bloody boys will snaffle zem up, an' sell zem again to 'ees competition.'

'What does he *mean*, "next week"?' asked Miss Elizabeth, haughtily.

'Yer, well, 'e's comin' back, inee?' said Henry Catchpole. ''e knows a bleedin' good fing when 'e sees it, doesn't 'e? You've made 'is bleedin' day orlright, buying that lot.'

'Let him come, and we'll buy his damned cage as well. It's cruelty to keep lovely birds caged up all their lives just so people can hear them sing outside their windows. If they want to hear birdsong they should go to the country or buy a record of *In a Monastery Garden*.'

The stallholder gathered up the little cages which housed the birds he sold to the public, and the big empty cage, and started to load his battered van. The crowds drifted away as the midday hour approached and it was time to eat.

Miss Elizabeth and Miss Angela strode off through the market, having done their good deed for the day, and the others returned to the café.

'You're all invited to a party at oor hoos on Sunday,' said Champagne Jock. 'Ah've got some guid stuff, some Moët and even some of the widow Cliquot.'

''ere - where do you get all that bleedin' champers?' asked Henry Catchpole.

'Wouldn't you like to know, baby? Wouldn't you like to *know*?' said Jock. 'an' by the way, if any of youse are goin' on your holidays, a've got a couple o' guid big leather suitcases for sale. Bargain prices to ma friends.'

As Henry Catchpole had said, McGinn's 'family' were coming out soon, but he had guessed that her father, Rex, and his twin brother Max were dead set against them leaving Hampstead to live with an ex-journalist, unknown novelist, well-known Hampstead drinkist, who was fifteen years older than Carolyn whom he had met on the doorstep of Keith Burgess's flat (formerly the home of M.P. Michael Foot, who had given it to Camden Council for a song to house the homeless) opposite the police station on Haverstock Hill, when McGinn saw that she had a bicycle pump in her hand and thought: 'No more paying for cabs,' with a mercenary chuckle. But within a week he was so in love with her he would have sold his flat to buy her a ticket to the moon. And her son, Rupert, seven, had impeccable manners. Childless couples and elderly couples queued to invite him for a weekend.

Rex and his twin Max were being told stories about McGinn: that he had slept with a nutritionist, Maureen, after stealing a flashing light from the roadworks near the house in Highgate to enliven the bedroom with a psychedelic light show, and, waking at dawn, had donned his hush puppies and Maureen's mauve silk negligee, the nearest item of clothing, and had called, 'Good morning', to a startled woman neighbour as he trotted back to the road works with the flashing orange lamp.

They had also been told that he often sipped a pint pot of hot consommé soup while lying in the bath to cure his hangover, and on a recent occasion, having been able to obtain only Heinz tomato soup, had balanced it on the edge, slid into the bath of soothing warm water only to have the pint pot fall into the bath so that he lay, contemplatively, for several minutes in a bath full of very thin tomato soup.

While Max ordered lemonade in the famous Magdala bar (scene of the murder by Ruth Ellis of her racing driver lover), and spiked it with whisky from his hip flask, Rex - the twins were called 'The Book Ends', like two Alsation dogs - ordered champagne for the whole bar in Soho and spent a fortune on his *Quatorze Juillet* (14th of July) birthday party in a nearby French restaurant. The handsome *boulevardier* Rex had been an art student in Paris in the '30s, but the war found him struggling back from Dunkirk and sending a Woodbine packet with the words AM SAFE - REX to his family. In London, as a highly paid advertising man, he had had a brief affair with Marlene Dietrich, who had fallen for him when he did the British Overseas Airways Corporation advert for legroom aboard their 'planes, showing Marlene with her gorgeous legs up on display.

Eventually, with the comment, 'Rupert will end up speaking patois', he gave in to Carolyn's wishes.

She said: 'He would have preferred me with a younger man - someone he could control. He took one look at you and knew he could never control you.'

McGinn had noticed how well-dressed Rex was. Silk suits and silk ties and shirts by Thresher and Glenny, and it was these clothes that led to some confusion much later when Carolyn had to return in haste from France for Rex's funeral, for his companion, Maggie, had given all Rex's clothes to Max. As the founder of Voice Over, the first voice-dubbing company, which gave a lot of work to thespians, the 'wake' for Rex in the Dorchester Hotel was packed with friends and clients, which led to unbelievable histrionics when Max walked in dressed in Rex's clothes. There were cries of: 'My God, he's back' and actresses fainted at the sight, until Carolyn introduced the twin brother they had not known existed.

All this was to come later. McGinn was 'emigrating' for the second time. He gave his furniture to Richard and Roddy Dawkin and popped into The Flask to catch up on the latest gossip. Frank Smyth, still following in George Gissing's footsteps in Grub Street, had not lost his penchant for gate-crashing Embassy parties. The Queen Mother was to attend one at the African Embassy, but Smyth had only old clothes. A customer in The Intrepid Fox, Frank's 'local' at that time, said: 'Try Louis, the tailor off Carnaby Street, Frank. He'll lend you a suit. Mention my name.'

Sure enough the little tailor had a suit which fitted Smyth perfectly. It had been ordered by the comedian, Al Read, and never collected.

At the Embassy that night, Frank stood, drink in hand, near the staircase when the Queen Mother entered a few minutes after him. He was surprised to receive a beaming smile from her and she chuckled behind a gloved hand and moved on. The giant African Embassy official next to Smyth, said, out of the corner of his mouth: 'Great set of threads, man.' Another, from Ghana, whispered: 'That's some suit, sir. Who's your tailor?'

Other guests looked curiously at Smyth beneath the chandelier, so he went to find a mirror, compelled by curiosity, and beheld himself in a suit that glowed, like a bullfighter's suit of lights, a fluorescent blue, and it suddenly dawned on him that the little tailor had mentioned that Al Read had ordered it for an appearance at the London Palladium, and it was made with cloth that lit up on stage under spotlights.

But the bar in Flask Walk was changing, and there were new faces who had replaced the old ones who were now scattered to the four winds.

For McGinn, another world was waiting - in the land of troubadours and wine, where Rabelais had written Gargantua and Pantagruel, and Julius Caesar had completed his education; where the Kings of France had walked in cobbled streets, and Molière drank with his friend the barber; where Clive of India had stayed and invented a local pastry, *Le petit pâté de Pézenas*; where McGinn had to go soon to take an exam for his hunting permit and buy an annual fishing licence, and finish building the house he had called *'Le Maquis'*, partly out of respect and partly because of its view of the hills of Holmes oaks where resistance men had hidden, beyond the valley of the butterflies.

Best of all, he would be *'en famille'*, for Carolyn and young Rupert would soon be packing the two suitcases and eight Sainsbury's plastic bags, their presence in the taxi to Victoria Station eliciting the comment from the driver: 'I like your Gucci luggage, Madam.'

The Valley of The Butterflies

Polishing the beams for a new roof on 'Le Maquis'. Raymond restores the ancient wine 'cuve' where the foundations are Roman and Saracen. Winter, 1980.

Lunch, during building, at the table made from 100-year-old floorboards, removed to make the sunken living room. Author with Carolyn and Rupert.

Sol y Sombra (Sun and Shade) in the house they built.

CHAPTER FIVE

THE changing seasons were more noticeable in France than in other countries because of the emphasis on food and the foodstuffs that come into season as the year progresses. Town dwellers forget that there is a season for eggs, and in country villages the eggs suddenly get bigger at Eastertime. The *'reveillon'* or all-night feasting which ushers in the New Year is celebrated with sea-food and shellfish and preserves of duck and goose. The autumn is a time for all the fresh fruit: grapes, peaches, melons, plums. June is the season for strawberries and asparagus.

In the Languedoc, July and August are the season for feasts in every village, enormous grills of mussels and sausages and cutlets with mountains of fresh salad and veritable fountains of wine, and this *fête* is called a *'brasucade'* for everything is cooked on a charcoal or *sarments* brazier, the great pans of mussels sprinkled with white wine and the meat cooked with thyme and rosemary, scenting the village air and tickling the taste-buds and causing dogs to howl in anticipation. Another word for a feast such as this is a *'mechoui'*, the marginal difference being that a whole sheep is roasted on a spit and the Arab spicy mutton sausage called *'merguez'* is served with the salad.

The village children become excited as the date of the first *'brasucade'* approaches, usually coinciding with Bastille Day, 14th July. In the school, the teacher set the children a project to finish before the holidays began: a picture compiled with wild flowers and feathers.

'But where will I get the feathers?' asked Rupert, just turned eight years. 'The wild flowers are easy - just down the road a little, but feathers...'

'In the hunting season they'd all be plucking quail and partridge and woodcock,' McGinn said, 'but right now - how about chicken feathers?'

'I suppose so...'

'You could ask Monsieur Marcel, the neighbour. He's not sulphating because he's semi-retired, so he'll be there now.'

'Will you come with me?'

'Oh, your French is good enough...'

'I know what to ask for, but...'

'All right then, if you're shy, come on.'

Rupert had learnt his French during six months at the Alliance Francaise on the Spanish island of Ibiza, a school rigidly within the French educational system but bizarre in discipline on dress. He had asked his mother: 'Can I wear my Boy Scout uniform to school today?' and when Carolyn asked: 'Will the school allow it?' he replied: 'I don't see why not - a kid came to school yesterday dressed as Batman.'

Monsieur Marcel listened gravely to the request for feathers then took Rupert by the hand and led him down into the chicken pen while McGinn waited in the street above.

'Ca suffit! Ca suffit!, Monsieur,' he heard him call, and he came back up the steps holding half a dozen white feathers in his hand, frowning.

'He picked up a chicken and started pulling the feathers out of its tail,' said Rupert, clearly shocked by such barbarity. 'I told him I'd got enough after two but he went on and pulled six out. It didn't half squawk.'

'He'd better watch out, or I'll set Gert and Daisy onto him.'

Rupert laughed: 'They'll probably hit him with their brollies.'

'So what events are you entering in the Fête?' McGinn asked him.

'All of them: ducking for apples in a basin of water, running with a trayful of empty beer bottles in a race, and pulling the funniest face. Also, guessing the ham.'

Guessing the ham was an annual event at the *fête* when a whole mountain ham was hung in a tree near the *Mairie* and for five francs you guessed the height of the ham. This event raised more than five hundred francs and paid towards the *brasucade*, which was a free feast for all residing in the village on the night of *Quatorze Juillet*, paid by the *Mairie*.

On the day before the *fête,* there was an invitation to lunch at the beach near Grau d'Agde where Monsieur and Madame Lemure had a large caravan on one of the scores of patches of land the local people used as summer weekend residences. Carolyn swam off the nearby beach and they ate grilled sardines freshly landed at the banks of the Herault river that morning, and drank *Picpoul de Pinet*, a dry white wine from a nearby village.

When the time came to return, Rupert did not want to leave the sandy beach and the seaside, so he was allowed to stay the night in the caravan. The night was so hot that the door of the caravan was left open, and when Rupert was returned next day McGinn and Carolyn did not recognise him. His head had changed into a football.

'The mosquito,' said Madame Lemure, 'is very savage in these parts. They breed in the Camargue in the *etangs*, the shallow lakes, and although they are bombed with insecticide every season, many survive, as you can see.'

Carolyn looked at her only son, shocked by his appearance, his face resembling a suet pudding, blotched with red, eyes closed.

In the evening, the order went out that everyone had to bring four things to the *brasucade*: a chair, a knife and fork, and an appetite. Seating was behind the school, and the fire, built in the ditch opposite, was supervised by the Mayor and the councillors, all of them experts at stirring the *sarments* to get just the right fierce heat before lowering on what looked like a wire mattress from a double bed, covered with pork sausages. While they were cooking, *pâté* was served and then *moules cru*, and the men of the village all produced well-used pocket knives, clasp knives with bone and horn handles and the popular Opinel wooden-handled knife with tin shield known as a Marseilles Toothpick. These were skilfully used to open the raw mussels. Next came cooked mussels in white wine and shallots, followed by the sausages and then cheese and cake and unlimited rosé and red wine with each course. Then the serious drinking and dancing started.

There were one or two foreign visitors who were staying with friends: a voice, that of a schoolteacher on holiday, was heard to say in English: 'That was the best sausage I've ever tasted in my life,' then she danced with all the men of the village, bringing applause from the men and jealous flashing glances from their wives and girl friends as she swayed to the rhythm of the music, fashionably dressed, bringing a touch of North London to South West France.

The children and teenagers sang and danced and shouted and chased each other and had a wonderful time until the younger ones were called to bed at midnight. By one o'clock the older villagers and couples had peeled off and gone to rest, but the merriment continued into the small hours as dawn ushered in Bastille Day and the fierce red eye of the sun came over the vines.

There was an eerie silence in the village that morning as Rupert accompanied McGinn to the site of the previous night's festivities in order to recover the three chairs they had taken to the feast. The bleary-eyed councillors were washing glasses and throwing bottles into rubbish sacks and generally tidying up and they were shown an open door of a room that contained the chairs. Looking inside, the first impression was of entering a wood-shed with all the kindling wood piled haphazardly in the centre. This heap of splintered and broken sticks, it turned out, was the chairs from the night before, after the dancers and revellers had taken a nose-dive into them from time to time.

In a cardboard box were about fifty assorted knives and forks, a few pocket knives, a pair of false teeth, a mouth-organ, a leather wallet containing six hundred and fifty francs, two lipsticks, a powder compact, a tennis ball, and a bugle. If anything, the odd object out was the bugle, for it was part of the scratch 'orchestra' made up of village teenagers who inflicted pain on the eardrums pretending to play 'tunes' outside each house to collect money at the end of the four-day *fête*. McGinn was tempted to take it and hide it, making one less addition to the cacophony inflicted on the ears annually by the amateur 'orchestra'.

They were given plenty of time to recover, for the children's events started at four in the afternoon. The men of the village and their visiting families, practised *boules* in the main street which was sealed off to the traffic, or on the tiny *bouledrome* near the cemetery or the main one by two perfectly preserved medieval pack-horse bridges which bore the legend in huge letters: *VIVE LA PETANQUE*, a sure indication of bowling fanaticism in the village. Somehow McGinn could not imagine a similar notice in an English village: LONG LIVE LAWN TENNIS or LONG LIVE SHOVE HA'PENNY.

The children's games and races were being supervised by a couple of councillors and their wives and, of course, the *garde-champêtre,* who liked to be around when any supervision was to be done. As it was a *fête,* however, he had left his official *képi* at home. The race with the trays of empty beer bottles was run between the *Mairie* annexe which contained tools and a long wooden ladder attached to the wall, and the orchestra stand that had been set up in the main street.

Above the trestle tables which served as a bar, high in a plane tree, hung the mountain ham in all its glory, the secret of its height would be revealed by *Monsieur Le Maire* who had placed it there before the *fête,* using the village ladder, and he would officially measure its height using a ten-metre tape on the final day of the *fête.* The Mayor himself kept the blue exercise book in which were written the names and guesses in metres and centimetres of all contestants who had paid five francs to partake.

When the fragments of empty beer bottles had been swept up after the first race, it was time for the ducking for apples, and the huge red apples were placed in the bottom of a *sceaux,* a tough plastic bucket used to hold grapes in the *vendange.* The trouble was the apples were big and the children's mouths were small, and this necessitated staying under water while desperately trying to get a grip with tiny teeth on the polished smooth skin of the apple. Girls did not bother to even attempt the feat, but five francs was a lot of money to the village boys: they could buy a whole packet of American cigarettes with it and secretly smoke them at dusk on the *Mairie* steps, the height of sophistication.

Gasping for breath as he came up, Rupert failed; so did his friends Laurent and Luxilion the Portuguese boy, and it was the turn of Jean-Jacques to grip that apple with his teeth.

Little Jean-Jacques was keen to win the five francs. His determination to get a fix on that apple made him stay under water so long that people were beginning to think he was practising for a future evading the police in Venice.

'Pull him out,' suddenly called one of the councillors who had the sense to realise the little tiddler was on his way to drowning himself for five francs.

A councillor's wife who had nursing training pumped his chest and a spurt of water shot out of his mouth, his eyes opened and he grinned. With sighs of relief, one of the councillors pushed the apple into Jean-

Jacques' hand and said: 'You win. Don't try that again. You'll give us heart attacks.'

Monsieur le Maire was to judge the funny face competition. The village boys practised before the event, twisting lips and squinting eyes into horribly contorted masks. They were told to line up and get ready for the Mayor, who had been enjoying a family lunch and *digestifs* well into the afternoon. He came out of his house smiling, and strolled towards the waiting line-up. Looking closely at them as he arrived, he stepped up to Rupert, lifted his hand above his head and said: 'The winner.'

'But we haven't started yet,' said the *garde-champêtre.*

'Look at his face,' said the Mayor and they had to agree that this particular face, with puffed-up, semi-closed eyes, swollen cheeks and neck with lunar-red blemishes and fiery spots where the Camargue-bred mosquitoes had done their work, would be impossible to beat.

The lull in the evening which followed the children's games and the opening of the bar and tuning up of the orchestra was filled by 'practising' the game of *boules* in preparation for the prize at the end of the *fête.* Sometimes a professional *petanque* player would appear on the scene. He could be spotted by the highly-polished leather pouch that contained the *boules*, and his superior air as he regarded the local competition. He was usually better dressed than the village men, for professional *petanque* players in the South of France make a good living, and some big towns give a top prize equivalent to the price of a new car. French doctors have two standard remedies for a variety of illnesses: horse meat for any run-down or anaemic condition, and *petanque* for liver trouble and rheumatic pains, helped by the bending and stretching for the *boules.* Corpulent players ignore doctors' orders by using a magnet on a string rather than do a knees-bend.

As the hour of apéritif approached, it was time to make a dash to another village for a sight which would have gladdened the heart of Busby Berkeley and his trained dancing girls: a score of local fat men, many of them firemen, all bearing a close resemblance to the Michelin Man, dressed as drum *majorettes*, parading and countermarching down the main street as the crowds fall onto the pavement with laughter at the sight. Their trainer and leader, Jean-Pierre, *routier* and garage attendant, black-bearded and permanently smiling, throws the *baton* high into the air and skilfully catches it as trumpets play and drums beat and the team of fatties twist and turn and march with perfect timing past the packed terraces of the Grand Café and the Café de Commerce.

As dusk falls, the orchestras in the village strike up and a few bold dancers take the floor while the young men get their nerve up at the bar with beer and *muscat*. The parents and elderly couples are ready for the first course of the evening meal and clutch coloured tickets representing *hors d'oeuvre*, main course, salad, cheese, cakes, coffee.

The whole village was gathered together in the main street; babies in prams, toddlers, teenagers, parents, grandfathers and grandmothers, great grandfathers and great grandmothers, and, amazingly, one family of five generations, from a baby to a great-grandfather, this patriarch of ninety-two still capable of climbing a fruit tree to prune it in season. There were also aunts and uncles and cousins and distant relatives from the intermarriage between villages, and the generation gap existed only inasmuch as they divided naturally into groups: young wives gossiping, teenage boys plotting and smoking and drinking, young men who had been in the Army together, the *'troisieme age'* looking on benignly.

Through all this came the streaker.

Stark naked and well torched-up on the local brew, he tore down the main street to the yells of encouragement from his pals who were clearly betting him that he wouldn't dare to do it. There were shrieks from teenage girls, laughter from the grape farmers, curious glances from the young wives, calls of derision from the boys: 'You forgot your pants,' and 'The nude beach is that way,' and 'cretin' and 'idiot'.

The orchestra struck up, more and more dancers crowded the arena, laughing at the antics of the streaker, inhibitions broken down by the food and the wine and the ambiance and the thumping brassy music. Friends were beginning to arrive from other villages and the bar was crowded as five barmen tried to cope with the rush. Champagne was being ordered by the visitors. The eyes of the girls flashed at the men who looked over their shoulders at the groups of girls with their make-up perfect and their hair done, showing off their best dresses looking for future partners, looking their most beautiful in the light and shadow cast from the lamps in the trees and from the orchestra stand and its psychedelic patterns.

As visitors arrived at the bar they would order a drink and then look up into the tree, stand back a pace, and regard the hanging ham up there in the leaves. Then the guessing would start: a carpenter or a plumber would be sought, someone with a good eye for measurements, and serious discussion would take place before entries were made in the Mayor's blue exercise book and five francs handed over.

Spider Smith arrived and treated all his friends to a guess each, and then treated everyone in sight to champagne.

'How's the building going, then, Spider?' someone asked.

'I've got the roof on. Hope it's all right. I don't want to issue my missus and kids with umbrellas every time they take a bath or go to bed. Trouble is, I haven't got the bottle to go up and check it, and when you're employing mates who are working black, there's no guarantee like with a proper *entrepreneur* who gives you a ten-year guarantee with a roof.'

'Who's done it then?'

'Bash.'

There was a stony silence, interrupted only by the orchestra striking up again.

'Ah, well,' someone else said, 'umbrellas aren't all that expensive - the cheapo Hong Kong ones that is.'

When the laughter died, Spider said: 'I'm still gettin' stick from my neighbour though. She does go on. I think she's threatenin' to take me to court about the noise or somethin'. She don't 'alf slam them shutters when I start the mixer up.' He ordered another bottle of champagne and filled everyone's glass. 'I don't suppose it would do any good,' said Spider thoughtfully, a smile around his lips, 'but I could offer to get 'er surgically deafened like the King's Troop gun horses in Hyde Park, to stop 'er worryin'.'

'Somebody's waving at you,' said one of Spider's friends, nudging McGinn. It was Monsieur Marcel, the man with the watering-can, sitting at the family table where they had continued drinking after the meal.

'I've seen you with fishing rods, have I not? asked Monsieur Marcel when McGinn sat down. 'If you like fishing,' he continued without waiting for a reply, 'meet a master fisherman, who knows the sea, the rivers and the lakes.'

'Manouche,' said a tall, gangling, fair-haired man who sat with his family.

'He's from the north of France, but he is a true *paysan* who understands the country and the land.' He put his hand to his lips, 'Oh, and the sea as well.'

'I couldn't make a living out of the sea,' said Manouche, lighting an American cigarette.

'We'd fish all night and all next day and land a load of sardines, then two smart boys would come along and offer a derisory sum per kilo and it was take it or leave it and they had the refrigeration space to take them. Either we accepted their price or we threw them back in the sea before they rotted on the harbour. We were trapped in their net. So I gave it up.'

'It's the same in the vegetable and fruit market,' McGinn said. 'A new grower waits all day and at the last minute the wide boys come and offer a third of the market price and you take it or leave it. I went there with Raymond and he gave Martine's courgettes to friends rather than sell them for next to nothing.'

'If you want to go fishing, I'm trying the River Orb tomorrow,' said Manouche.

'One moment. I'm sorry, you've got nothing to drink,' said Monsieur Marcel, reaching for a clear bottle of white wine on the table.

'What is that?' McGinn asked, and Monsieur Marcel put his right index finger to his lower right eyelid and pulled with that knowing look.

'Taste,' he said.

The wine came out of the bottle clear and luminous, carefully poured by the man who had made it. It tasted like liquid gold, as if a spirit were laying gold leaf on the tongue and letting it roll down the throat, making the taste buds jump with joy. The gold colour of it crackled lights of fire through the bottle as Monsieur Marcel carefully replaced the cork, fastening in once more the ghosts of ancestral wine growers and acolytes of Bacchus temporarily released into the glass.

'*Nom de Dieu.*'

'Ah. That is wine. Grenache, ten years old, matured in oak, drawn this morning for Quatorze Juillet. It is the one we keep for ourselves.'

'I'd like to buy a bottle,' said Manouche.

'We never sell it.'

'Do you like trout?'

'Now you are talking. That may be interesting.'

'We must see what we can do.'

'Agreed.'

Monsieur Marcel uncorked the pride of his wine cellar and poured two more glasses of the sparkling bright trickling topaz and Manouche and McGinn sipped carefully.

'How do you find it?' asked Monsieur Marcel.

'There was once a team of French scientists in Russia,' said Manouche, 'and they dug up a mammoth, perfectly preserved in the ice, and, being French, they cooked some and ate it. One of them, asked to describe the taste, said: "It tastes of eternity." This wine tastes of paradise.'

'Liquid gold,' McGinn said, 'brushed by the wings of butterflies.'

Monsieur Marcel, clearly pleased by the compliments to his art, uncorked the vintage grenache and poured two more glasses.

'Would you exchange four bottles of this for that mountain ham hanging in that tree?' said Manouche, pointing across the road.

Monsieur Marcel shrugged. 'I have ham in the house. Trout - now that's a much more interesting proposition. Anyway - you'd have to win it first.'

'Oh, I'll win it all right.'

'You sound very confident, Monsieur Manouche. Has my grenache gone to your head?'

'Yes, but that's not the reason: a fisherman has to be able to judge distance. I also work as a painter and interior decorator, constantly using the tape measure. I am sure I can win it.'

'Good luck, but, you know, my wife has a recipe for trout with garlic and parsley that would make your mouth water.'

'With garlic? Never! With almonds perhaps, or a little butter and parsley, a little lemon squeezed on...'

'It's done in the Aveyron, up there in the hills where they have the best trout in France. My wife got the recipe from a chef in Brusque...'

'Is it fried or grilled?'

'Neither. It is simmered in white wine and you prepare the garlic...'

'Excuse me,' McGinn said. 'I'll just have a word with a friend at the bar.' They would talk for an hour about how to cook trout, exchange recipes, compare white wines, recall past meals in minute detail, recommend restaurants to each other.

'I'll call for you at five a.m. We'll fish the Orb and a couple of tributaries.'

'Five?'

'Of course. Before the first light. Best time.'

'Right, and can I bring young Rupert along?'

'It goes without saying. A boy should have a dog and a fishing rod. Did I not see him with two friends going to the quarry yesterday? They had a little black and white bitch with them.'

'That's right. T.F - *toujours faim*, that's her name.'

'That's the sight I like to see, boys with fishing rods going off for the day, but you should get him some mosquito repellent. He's been badly bitten. It's the season for them on the coast, in the lakes. Only the females bite, you know, when they're pregnant. Incidentally, how do you think the fish got into that water in the quarry?'

'I was wondering about that. It's a bit of a mystery.'

'No mystery. I put them there. It's what I like to do, swell the fish population in the region.'

Manouche looked smug. There was no doubt that he had one hundred percent confidence in himself. He knew it all. He was sure he would win the ham. Would a sudden flash of lightning convert him from Supermanouche into a humble learner?

'The female mosquitoes in the Camargue have something to learn from the ones I've seen in India, Manouche,' McGinn said. 'They actually push their babies through the holes in the mosquito nets so they can practise on the tourists.'

'What's that?' asked Monsieur Marcel, looking puzzled. 'Is it possible?'

Manouche's mouth hung open, but he quickly recovered his aplomb and said: 'It's a joke, Monsieur Marcel. It's called *le humeur Anglais*.'

Spider Smith was still splashing out champagne at the bar. 'Come and 'ave a drink,' he called.

'No thanks, I'm having an early night. I'm going fishing in the morning.'

'Don't talk to me about money,' he was saying to one of his friends at the bar. 'With what I've paid Bash and spent on that house, I could have had a good holiday in Thailand...'

In the small hours of the morning the band stopped playing but the village continued to celebrate. During the four days of the *fête* not much sleep was had by anyone, and after that there would be other villages to visit, for work on the land had virtually ceased until the harvest in September.

All was silent, however, at five in the morning when Manouche's car came to a stop outside the house. He tapped lightly on the door and they joined him carrying fishing rods, *pâté* and tomatoes from the fridge, a camembert cheese, a *glacier* containing bottles of wine and a thermos flask of coffee. A sleepy-eyed Rupert managed to doze off again in the back of the car as they drove, headlights on, through the vines, towards the distant hills.

'What bait will we use?' McGinn asked Manouche.

'Depends,' was his laconic reply.

'The *tabac* that sells maggots in the next village doesn't open until seven.'

'Buy maggots?' he said, astonished by the suggestion, 'If I want maggots I leave out the skin of a rabbit or the remains of an old camembert, but the Mare river which runs into the Orb is first category trout fishing, so maggots are forbidden.'

'So what will we use? All I brought was some stale bread.'

'That's good. I have some as well. The café keeps it specially for me. We'll use that this afternoon, maybe in the Herault. It's not as fast flowing as the Orb.'

Manouche was keeping his counsel, but McGinn knew he had much to learn from him. His fishing rods were painted white, for night sea fishing, and his reels were Mitchells, the best quality. His own rods and reels and waders had been bought at bargain prices in Andorra and Rupert's beginner's rod had been bought in Spain in a sale.

They followed the course of the Mare, through ancient Roman villages which once had silver mines, past one of the four hundred bridges in France which had the same name: *Le Pont de Diable*, the devil's bridge, which divided the river into first and second class fishing; north of the bridge only natural bait could be used. They stopped the car at a ford, with Rupert still asleep in the back seat. Manouche took a torch and a glass jar. He turned over stones and took from the slimy underside tiny shrimps before they could scuttle off the stone. Further upstream under trees he turned more stones and found tiny twigs, which, broken open contained a fat maggot, called *porte-bois* or *porte-faix*. When the jar was nearly full, they drove towards the woodland, for the vines had ended in the foothills, and parked in a farmyard where Rupert awoke and helped carry the rods and bags.

'Walk like thieves in the night,' said Manouche in a whisper. 'Not a sound, and stay behind the rocks while we bait the hooks.' By torchlight, in total silence, he put the hooks into the little shrimps, then he cast over the rocks into the big deep pool below, spanned by a concrete bridge. A faint glimmer of morning light began very slowly to suffuse the valley, and then, at the east end of the valley where no trees obscured the horizon, the first ray of sun struck towards them.

'Clack,' said Manouche, and gave a heave on his rod, firmly fixing the hook into the mouth of the fish.

McGinn looked at his watch. It was two minutes past six on the 15th of July. exactly the legal time - until 9.30 p.m. - to catch fish, restricted exactly to the hours of daylight. Was Manouche showing off? He looked smug as he wound in the fish, but disappointed when there was a *gardon* struggling on the hook instead of a big fat trout. 'Merde,' he said softly to himself, and expertly removed the *gardon*, slipped it into his fishing bag, quickly baited the hook and cast once more over the rocks. By now the dawn chorus of birds filled the valley, and the eye of the sun, peeping over the horizon was filling the valley with bright light, and revealing the big boulders and rocks that made the valley bed as white as dried bones, with the crystal-clear water gushing white over pebbles to send bubbles of froth eddying downriver over placid pools on either bankside. There was no need for Manouche to hush them to be quiet, for they were witnessing a little part of paradise in the by now sun-drenched valley.

Suddenly, and startlingly, a kingfisher alighted on the tip of McGinn's fishing rod. Rupert had the sense not to exclaim at the wonderful sight, or to call out. Manouche remained motionless as they watched its black bright eye flicker, regarding the pool below, then, as quickly as it had appeared, it had disappeared, diving down into the pool to catch a minnow and flitting off, from bush to bush on the opposite bank, back to its secret nest in the bankside. It had rested on the rod for only four seconds, but provided a lifetime's memories, a sight as rare as that of a red squirrel.

'You see what happens when you keep still and quiet in the country?' said Manouche. 'Always remember, Rupert, to walk quietly, and stay back from the river bank. Fish can detect vibrations, and if you can see them, they can see you.'

They fished quietly for an hour, Manouche becoming more and more disappointed as they caught another gudgeon and baited up with the tiny shrimp, then switched to *porte-bois* and Manouche caught a barbel which cheered him up a little. He crouched in full concentration at the task of catching fish, a thin blade of a man, tall and angular with frizzy blonde hair, aquiline features, the sensitive hands and mouth of an artist, and by his side his fishing bag, filled with homemade floats of green and brown and blue plastic or long floats made from turkey feathers. He had muttered a word under his breath when he had caught the gardon, which McGinn took to be an Alsace word for the fish, for that was the region where Manouche had fished with gypsies and learnt the lore of the rivers and the banksides and the forests; he had learnt from them the art of trapping frogs and gathering mushrooms and truffles, and also the art of poaching.

'The water's too low,' announced Manouche, starting to reel in and pack up his gear. 'We'll try the Orb. I must get trout today for your neighbour. The tributaries are too shallow in summer.' There was no question of discussion or argument; the apprentices had to follow the leader over the rocks and through the bushes back to the car. They drove back along a road lined with cherry trees, already harvested, past rocks carved skilfully into human faces by a local sculptor, through the valley of peach trees in the foothills of one of the largest cherry orchards in Europe, the fruit exported annually to Germany to make *kirsch*, over the crossroads and down the valley of the Orb passing a signpost for the forest of the Writers, the trees dedicated to the literary men who fought in the resistance or died in uniform, *les Ecrivains Combattants*.

On the bankside of the Orb, Manouche took a sack from the car, unloaded the glaciers and transferred the fish into the ice cubes of one and put the food in the other.

'What's the sack for?' Rupert asked him as he attached it to his belt so that it hung from his hip.

'For the fish.'

With his unbounded optimism he set off up the bank and down into the river and they followed, splashing across pebble banks where McGinn noticed water-cress growing. 'We could have a nice *soupe de cresson* tonight, Manouche - before the trout.'

McGinn took a leaf, halved it and gave him one half to taste, for he could see he was not very sure about the cress. He nibbled the leaf: 'You don't see it on sale in France any more,' he said. 'There was a scare when some was found to be contaminated.'

'Only if there are sheep in the area,' McGinn said. There are no sheep in the Orb valley to contaminate the water. Cress is contaminated by the fluke in a sheep's liver getting into the water.'

On the bankside opposite, a middle-aged man was fishing near a wooden hut which was probably his weekend hideaway or camping spot. 'There's nothing much in here,' he called out to the trio. 'I've been at it since seven. No luck.'

Manouche, dragging the now wet sack hanging from his hip, waded into the middle of the river with the current splashing against the backs of his knees and opened the jar containing the bait and released it into the water. Then he pulled pieces of bright green moss from the rock and put it in the jar, and then pulled handfuls of moss from the rock and let it float downstream. He baited their three hooks with pieces of moss the size of a little fingernail.

He pointed to where they were to position themselves in the river, spaced out, and McGinn watched his technique as he put the float at eighty centimetres above the moss-covered hook and cast downstream, letting the current take the float. He cast twice more, then moved the float to a metre from the hook, cast again three times then moved the float to one metre fifteen centimetres and cast once more, and this time the float went under.

'Clack,' said Manouche in triumph as he hauled in his fish. 'It's not a trout,' he said. 'It's a *gardon*.' He unhooked the silver roach with the red fins and slipped it into the sack, cast again and watched as the float was dragged under once more. McGinn signalled to Rupert to put his float at the same distance, for the fish were feeding one metre fifteen centimetres beneath the surface and, a lesson they had suddenly learned, the fish, like many humans, turn vegetarian in summer. They were not interested in worms or maggots, but were gobbling up pieces of moss as it floated downstream. Half an hour before midday the sack was full. Manouche had caught seventy percent of the fish. Suddenly Rupert gave a cry. On his hook was a trout. Manouche waded over to him and took the trout off the hook. 'It's a bit small,' he said. 'Just within the limit. So you've caught your first trout, young man.' Rupert, his eyes shining, slipped the trout into his fishing bag. 'Lunchtime,' announced Manouche. 'You can grill the trout for your lunch,' he said to Rupert. 'And I guarantee that you will now be a fisherman for the rest of your life, and you'll never forget the day your first trout took the bait.'

'What will you do with all the fish in the sack?' Rupert asked. 'My cats,' said Manouche. 'I have eight of them, and they get very hungry, and tinned cat-food is expensive.'

As they left the river, McGinn gathered a plastic bag full of watercress. The man opposite was still fishing. 'Any luck?' Manouche called out to him. 'Not a thing. There's nothing in here,' he called back. Manouche asked McGinn to help him to haul the sackful of roach out of the river, for it was wet and heavy with about fifty fish in it. 'What's in the sack?' the man opposite called out.

'Fish,' shouted Manouche, a little smile lingering around the corners of his mouth and that old smug look on his face. He took a fat roach out of the sack and held it up and the man on the bank nearly fell in the river with shock. When he recovered, he called out: 'What bait were you using?'

'Moss,' shouted Manouche, but he may as well have shouted fourteen carat diamonds for the man clearly did not believe him.

They built a fire from the *sarments* found in a nearby vineyard and Rupert grilled his trout while Manouche cooked three hamburgers on a little wire grill he always carried in the boot of the car. 'Taste,' said Rupert and they each had a nibble.

'There's nothing like it in the world,' said Manouche. 'The taste of fresh river trout grilled on vine stalks.'

After they had eaten the hamburgers with slices of tomato, Manouche asked: 'What kind of meat do you think that was?'

'Beef, wasn't it?' McGinn said.

'No. Horse,' said Manouche, watching them and waiting for a reaction. Rupert made a face, but he had lived long enough out of England not to be shocked by people eating horsemeat.

'The British don't eat horsemeat, do they?'

'No, they love horses too much to be able to eat them. They don't eat frogs' legs either,' Rupert said.

'Ah, frogs' legs in garlic and parsley, or deep fried in batter and dipped in tomato purée. What could be nicer?' said Manouche, and, sitting back against the bankside, put a flaming twig to a Gauloises cigarette.

'The gypsies make money by catching frogs and selling them,' said Manouche, 'and one night I sat with them on top of the bankside of a stream, waiting for the moon to rise. The gypsies had fixed big sacks over dozens of holes in the bankside. I asked what we were waiting for, and they said when the moon reached a certain height, the frogs would leave their hiding places and try to get into the stream, and they would be trapped in the sacks. They knew that on a certain night when the moon was at a certain height it was a great attraction to the frogs, and sure enough, just as they said, I saw the sacks begin to move as dozens and dozens of frogs left the holes and jumped into the sacks. You have to live very close to the land to know tricks of nature like this.'

'The fish couldn't see us in the river, Manouche, that's why we caught so many, isn't it?' Rupert said.

'They feed in shoals in the current and... shhh...'

Manouche motioned us to silence, and pointed.

'*Couleuvre*,' he said. He had seen the movement of a grass snake in the shrubbery of the river bank, rose cautiously to his feet and, like a Red Indian stalking, went into the foliage. We heard a 'thwack' and he returned holding the dead snake.

'Why did you kill it, Manouche?' Rupert asked.

'Because I'm going to eat it.'

'Ugh.'

'Why ugh? In England you eat eels, don't you? What's the difference? This is an eel that lives on land, that's all.'

He put the snake in one of the plastic bags he always carried.

'And,' he added. 'I'll make a belt from the skin.'

'No-one eats fresh-water fish in this region,' McGinn said. 'They eat squirrels, and robins and grass snakes, thrushes, skylarks, blackbirds, and even a fox if they can catch one.'

'No flavour - unless you smoke them, preferably in wood chippings from the oak tree, and also too many little bones, too much work filleting them,' said Manouche, starting to pick up the *glaciers* which now contained the fish.

'I'm going to cheat now,' he said. 'They say the trout is the king of fish, but hard to catch, and when the water is low...' We moved down the bankside towards the car. 'In the rivers, we go to where the water is freshest and where there are sure to be trout. The Gorge d'Heric, not far from here.'

There were mountaineers practising in the gorge when they climbed the concrete stairway that led up the valley into the mountains, and several ramblers and groups of girls who sat, reading and knitting while they watched their boy-friends, like flies on the high cliff face.

'True love,' McGinn said to Manouche as they passed the girls, 'a mountaineer's groupie.'

'Or a fisherman's wife,' he said.

They passed a tiny copper pipe coming out of a rock that disgorged pure mineral water, the ramblers holding bottles to catch it and drink it, then higher up they climbed down the rocks towards a pool, clear and shallow. Manouche became furtive, watching the heights in case anyone could see them, and produced from his fishing bag a fine white nylon net which he proceeded to spread across the pool so that it sank onto the pebble bottom, then he took from the bag a phial with a tin cap, exactly the kind of phial used by the gypsies when selling wormwood essence to make moonshine *pastis*. He took an empty cigarette packet, put a pebble in it, tapped half the contents of the phial into it and screwed the top shut.

'What are you doing, Manouche?' Rupert asked.

'Something illegal,' he said, looking around again at the heights, searching for the movement of a fishing guard lurking in the bushes. 'I hope you can keep a secret. You mustn't talk about this at school or in the village. This is how the gypsies catch trout when they're hungry. It's against the law to sell fresh-water fish to restaurants. I'd get a very heavy fine for what I'm about to do...'

Having staked the net with sticks at the little waterfall from the gap where the pools above ran into the one he had netted, he threw the cigarette packet into the top end of the pool so that it sank and opened, releasing the mysterious powder into the water. He indicated to McGinn to take the other unattached end of the net and lifted it, blocking off the exit from the pool.

'Watch now, and you'll see an amazing sight,' said Manouche, his eyes constantly searching the rocks and bushes. 'This is first category fishing in this gorge,' he said. 'A man fishing illegally with maggots fishes with a cigarette in his mouth, so that if the guard appears he burns through the line to destroy the evidence. But with a net...' He left the sentence unfinished for the pool had started to boil with fighting trout. They saw them come through the gap in the boulders from the pool above, swarming towards the place where the cigarette packet had released the powder.

'Right, that's enough, pull the net with me,' Manouche called, and they drew the net towards the sticks attaching the top, hauling in a dozen trout, fighting and twisting and turning in the net. With another swift scanning of the valley, Manouche opened the sack he had earlier attached to his leg.

Very quickly, with a flick of his thumb in the gill to kill them instantly, he transferred the trout from the net to the sack, and then put the sack of fish into the *glacier*. He gathered together his belongings, the folded net and the fishing bag, and, with another furtive scanning of the heights, set off up the bankside, away from the scene of his crime. Back in the car, he lit a cigarette, appearing rather nervous, his long fingers twitching slightly.

'What was the powder, Manouche?' Rupert asked him.

'Ephemera,' he said, 'powdered may-fly. You know how trout rise to catch the may-fly as they hatch out in the evening and drop from the trees onto the surface of the river? The gypsies gather the may-fly in season and with a pestle and mortar grind the dried flies into a powder. The trout smell it in the river and go mad to get at it. It's a secret trick used by poachers.' McGinn smiled as he caught on.

'You're exchanging the trout for the *grenache*, aren't you?'

'Yes. I have an idea to market it in other countries, it's such a marvellous wine, and not very well known outside the Herault.'

'But why risk a fine poaching trout when you could have bought some from a fishmonger?'

'Buy fish? When the rivers are full of them? You might as well ask me to buy rabbits when they swarm here, or blackberries or quince or mushrooms when it's all free. No, the real reason is that Monsieur Marcel would have known they had been bought. He's a wily old French peasant.'

'By the taste, you mean?'

'Yes, that and something else. Wild trout have undamaged tails. Farm trout and tank trout in the shops have nibbled tails - nibbled by the other prisoners in the tank.'

'Why do they do that, Manouche?' Rupert asked.

'Frustration. Boredom. Being trapped, a wild thing, a game fish, trapped and unable to escape. Nibbling tails is like us scratching on a cell wall if we're trapped.'

He started the car. 'So what have we caught today? Don't count the trout, except Rupert's. I could have caught them, you know, but it would have taken two hours or more in the gorge, plus having to dig for worms...' He named the fish: gudgeon, roach, rudd, and grayling.

'The River Herault next, for tench, bream, Canadian perch.' He smiled. 'I will show Rupert how to catch most fish in the Languedoc rivers, and later we'll try for pike and zander, the game fish you do see on the menus of the restaurants here.'

Under the bridge that spanned the Herault, Manouche soaked great lumps of bread, then squeezed out the water until he had pieces the size of tennis balls, and threw them at intervals into the deep brown water of the pool near the bankside. They used only moistened bread for bait, and as the fish smelt the ground-bait Manouche had laid, they started to take enormous tench and bream. There was a sudden movement in the centre of the river, a small fish leaping three times out of the water as if being pursued by something.

'Zander,' said Manouche, and quickly reeled in, took his spinning rod, put a tiny silver spoon lure on it and was off up the bankside where he could wade in and cast right into the centre where the zander was feeding, chasing minnows and swallowing them whole. He stood in profile, long nose, chin up, concentrating on getting the lure in front of the cruising zander, reeling in, casting, his elbows and knees sticking out at angles.

After five minutes, with the surface of the river now still, indicating that the zander had gone downstream, Manouche reeled in and joined us on the bankside, where he opened up the *pâté* and made some snacks.

'*Goûter*,' said Rupert.

'That's right - this is your *"goûter"*, young man,' said Manouche, using the word for the afternoon snack - or morning snack - that all

French children take to school or buy at the school.

'We'll catch that zander another day, now I know where he is feeding,' said Manouche. 'Next time I'll use live bait - a minnow, irresistible to a hungry zander.'

On the way home, they stopped and caught some Canadian perch, brightly coloured green and brown with red fins.

'I'll fillet these for my supper,' said Manouche. 'They eat them in Switzerland a lot, but the filleting takes time and patience.'

'Why not the trout?'

'I stopped eating trout years ago as I'd had a surfeit of them. Any food becomes boring if you have too much of it.'

Back in the village, Manouche exchanged the trout for three bottles of grenache and Rupert took some of the gudgeon to feed his kitten whose name he had changed from *Mouche* to Midge. As McGinn and Manouche drove past the hanging ham, on their way for an *apéritif* in the village where Manouche was living, he looked at it and said: 'I'll have that ham on my table at the end of the *fête*, you wait and see. It will cost me the price of three bets.'

In the bar, they ordered *pastis*, and then Manouche excused himself, saying he was going to feed the cats.

In twenty minutes, Manouche was back, with that 'cat that got the cream' expression on his face.

'It'll be ready in fifteen minutes,' he said

'What will be ready in fifteen minutes?'

'The snake.'

'You've cooked it?'

'Of course. I have no fridge. I hope you like it.'

'My God,' McGinn said, 'snake and chips.'

'No chips, but new potatoes, garden peas, courgettes in flower, all from my neighbours. They have cats, you see, and I have fish, and they have gardens, and that's how it is arranged. Fresh fish for fresh vegetables.'

Manouche always had about him that supercilious air when he was successfully wheeling and dealing, especially if he was winning or about to win.

'Carolyn and I are eating at Le Vieux Coq in Pézenas tonight and Rupert's staying with friends in the village.'

'Try some, anyway. A new experience.'

He had braised it in white wine and parsley on a charcoal fire, for he did not buy bottles of gas for cooking, and there were several boxes of garden vegetables stacked around the kitchen. Manouche fell under the category of bohemian, the antithesis of *bourgeois*: he always washed up before the meal, taking whatever plates and cutlery were necessary from the pile in the sink. Beneath the old stone sink, eight cats of various sizes and colours tucked into fresh river fish, spread out on old newspapers.

Cautiously, McGinn tasted the dish.

'Well?'

'It doesn't taste of eternity and it doesn't taste of paradise. Veal, I would say. That's the nearest I can get to the flavour. Thanks, anyway.'

'Don't you want any more?'

'No, that's for you. I'm eating out later.'

McGinn noticed that he had tacked the skin of the grass-snake to a plank in order to dry it. On the table was a German machine for smoking fillets of fish on oak chippings. There were a couple of fillets inside it.

'Try some of that,' said Manouche, putting some of the *gardon* onto a plate. It was delicious, with a very delicate kipper flavour.

'I'll see you at the *fête* tomorrow, the last night,' he said. 'Next time we go fishing, we'll be picnicking on mountain ham.'

Manouche's confidence in himself was amazing. People were beginning to call him Supermanouche in the bar, where snippets of information about him had been retailed to McGinn by the bartender and one or two local people. Newly arrived in the village, he quickly became 'engaged' to a local girl, Mathilde, who worked in Geneva in an international organisation, so she could rarely live in her own house. Manouche had persuaded her to sign a contract, binding and legal under French law, that he, for his part, would install a bathroom, renew the floor and generally refurbish the place and she, for her part, would let him live there rent-free and if she were accidentally killed in a car crash, he would automatically inherit the house.

Was there anything Manouche spent money on, apart from cigarettes and the odd drink in the local bar? He virtually lived off the land, with his fishing and trapping and exchanging and bartering. He adamantly refused to buy a bottle of gas, and simply lit a fire for cooking. There was electric light. McGinn looked at the inside meter. He saw him looking. The meter wheel had stopped turning. He looked at the side and in the glass.

A miniscule hole had been drilled in the meter box and a piece of thin wire inserted to halt the wheel by holding the cogs. The hole was invisible for a touch of matching blue paint had been applied to it, and it would take only a second to remove the wire if an inspector from *Electricité de France* called.

'I hate E.D.F.' said Manouche. 'They are the greatest criminals in France. See what they have done to these villages and to the French countryside - posts and wires everywhere, a complete abortion. In other countries they can put the wires underground, but not E.D.F. the despoilers.' Manouche, the country-lover, sounded very angry. 'To branch electricity into a house half a kilometre from a main road costs more than the value of the house, then they ruin it by sticking great concrete posts across the land and outside the country house. I pay them nothing. They make enough money. Do you want another smoked fillet?'

'No, I'm off, Manouche, and thanks for a good day. I'm learning. So is Rupert. We'll make a fisherman of him.'

Back in the village there was pandemonium: men were running to their houses and coming out with shotguns.

'Be careful when you get out of the car,' someone shouted, 'There's a wild boar loose and he's wounded.'

Right:
Grape harvesters
celebrate the final day
by throwing the
author (with the help
of Raymond on the
right) into Gabian
fountain. The 'victim'
thoughtfully removes
his watch before the
soaking.

Below:
'We run them in...' The author 'arrests' Raymond, before they
swapped uniforms, at the entrance to the 15th Century Ghetto in
Pézenas. The start of the Pézenas carnival.

Photo: Christian Lesure

Patrice took his own apple wood to picnics to flavour the meat. The former paratrooper was arrested by 'The Sheriff' for shaving his head.

Alfie, the Irish porter who asked the name of the dead squirrel in the deep-freeze. Every year he borrowed the money for his ticket back to Rotterdam.

Right:
Jean-Paul, builder and expert plasterer. Bailiffs serving a maintenance order found a burnt-out shell - his *cabanon* in the vines - and nailed it to the charred doorpost.

Photo: Jane Craven

'Fell off the back of a lorry? That's genuine Katherine Hamnet schmutter, Madame. 'Course I 'ad to take the labels aht - wiv 'er permission...' Henry Catchpole (the late Ronnie Jones, singer and guitarist on French radio) does the market in Roujan. Or is he trying to sell Nipper, the photographer's Lakeland terrier, to the author?

Peter Kinsley

Photo: Peter Kinsley

Above:
Carolyn with Midge the cat.
His claw caught in a gin-trap.
The vet charged 400 francs,
causing the author to have his
cheque book invalidated by
the Banque de France.

Left:
Rupert 'gurning', but it was
the mosquito bites that got
him 1st prize in the village
compettion. Carolyn sees him
off from Montpelier airport
to Miami, Florida, via
London, a lone traveller,
aged 9.

Right:
Pause for a swim in the
Embalso (reservoir) de Yesa,
between Pamplona and Jaca,
the rainwater as blue as the
Mediterranean.

Below:
The author at St Jean-Pied-de-
Port, a brief stop in the tourist-
filled town.

Where it all started. A nostalgic visit to the House of the Musicians in Pézenas, scene of the author's first *vendange* with Raymond and Martine, whose famous father, Boby Lapointe, troubadour, lived just a few doors away. Francois Truffaut had to put sub-titles on his words in his films.

138

Right:
Author Peter Kinsley falls in
love with the Mediterranean
after seeing lemons and
oranges against a blue sea
background on Army leave
in Italy in 1954.
(See Vol. II of my memoirs,
*Don't Tell My Mother I'm a
Newspaperman*, p.284).

Photo: Barry Sawyer

Forty years on...

Peter Kinsley, 1994, assisted by the Mayor of Neffies, places a
'gerbe', a bouquet of flowers, on behalf of British Servicemen in the
Herault, on the plaque for Henri Mas, resistance leader of Roujan,
murdered in Buchenwald concentration camp by the Nazis in 1944.

Francois Courmont ('Francois the Fingers') whose girlfriend married Jean-Paul Chaudron. A leading French cave-explorer, Francois, colleague of Michel Siffre, gave the name 'Speleonautes' to their calling in 1962 when Siffre stayed two months isolated (simulating atomic attack survival) in the Alpes Maritimes, 130 metres down for 20,000 hours, aiding research in biology, medicine, science and military survival. Author Peter Kinsley was there as a journalist when Siffre was lifted by helicopter to Marseilles on 17 September 1962.

CHAPTER SIX

A S McGINN parked outside the house, Carolyn called: 'Come in quickly, there's a wild boar roaming around.' Inside the house she said: 'Rupert came face to face with the *sanglier* down in the valley of the butterflies. He was with Laurent and they had catapults. Luckily T.F. followed them down there and she barked and scared it. What happened exactly, Rupert?'

'We were practising with our catapults down on the footpath that enters the valley when a *sanglier* came out of a ditch. It had big tusks. It was enormous. We were dead scared. Then T.F. barked. She was brave. She ran at it and barked like mad and it turned and ran. It ran towards the village. A man shot it with a twelve-bore, but it was a *chevrotine* and he only wounded it and made it mad. It's down in the street below. They're all going to get their guns to kill it. Have you got bullets?'

'No, only *chevrotine*.' The neighbour who had fired at the animal had used buckshot, and the lead pellets had no effect on it other than to wound it and make it fighting mad. Hunters used a lead bullet in their shotguns for wild boar as hunting rules dictated only smooth bore guns could be used to give the animal a chance. A hunter had to be a crack shot to hit a running boar using this method.

'Run and get the American, Tex, up the steps. You know where he lives. Tell him to bring the Schmeiser and the Colt .45 - and bring Duke as well.'

Rupert was off running, over the road and up the cement steps that led to the top of the village. 'You're not going out there, are you?' Carolyn asked, her big worried brown eyes wide, watching McGinn get the guns out. There was a .22 rifle with a telescopic sight and a silencer, a single shot target gun he had bought to train Rupert how to shoot, the gun he had used to get his first rabbit, lying in ambush, but a useless weapon against a *sanglier*; and a Russian shotgun, 12-gauge, double-barrelled, a variety of numbered cartridges containing different weights of lead shot and black powder for large and small game birds, and two McGinn had forgotten about containing lead bullets given to him by Tex. He slipped the two into the breech of the Russian gun and went outside as Carolyn called, 'Be careful,' and closed the door.

Leaving the gun open, a legal nicety in French villages, he waited for the American, Tex Ranald, who owned a house near the church and had been for many years with the American forces in Germany, occasionally letting German friends use his house. Rupert was a fast runner, and he and Tex came down the steps rapidly, with the American thumbing the long cartridge with the pointed copper coated bullet into the breech and clicking the bolt as he reached street level. A Colt .45 hung from his hip in a leather holster.

'Did some asshole try and shoot an old shoat with buckshot? That's the worst thing he could have done. Might as well use a B.B. gun on him. Let's go get him before he kills a couple of chil'ren.' He called over his left shoulder: 'Come on, Dook, we may need you to corner him, boy.' The graceful hunting dog, a French *Braque* or pointer, a highly intelligent bird-dog, stayed close to Tex's heels as he swung down the hill to where the action was.

The *sanglier* had got itself between the side of a van and the parapet of a garden, in a narrow street that ran parallel to a stream, and it appeared to be about to make a run for it. Men leaned out of windows with shotguns or stood, half-hidden and wary, in doorways. Had Tex been five seconds earlier in reaching the level of the street, he could have shot it dead with the Schmeiser, for McGinn had seen him group eight bullseyes, an inner and a magpie at three times the distance, a crack shot with rifle and pistol and a highly experienced hunter.

Suddenly the wild boar made a run for it, and it ran a gauntlet of lead shot as men fired at it as it charged by. McGinn heard Tex groan and say: 'Tell them to stop firing, they're only making it worse.' But it was impossible to shout above the noise of the guns, and the animal was going so fast they knew he could not have hit it with a single bullet.

Luckily they were blocking the narrow street that would have allowed the boar to re-enter the village, and the presence of Tex's dog, Duke, made the animal pause in mid-flight for just enough time for Tex to draw a bead on it and press the hair trigger of the powerful rifle. McGinn saw Tex's right shoulder kick back with the force of the shot and weight of the weapon at the same time as the *sanglier* gasped its last breath. Before any of the other men could reach it, Tex strolled up to it and fired one shot of the .45 Colt as a *coup de grâce*. Then he turned away and came back to where Duke was obediently waiting for orders, nose twitching, eyes taking in every movement around.

'Let's go,' said Tex. 'What a bloody mess. I hate to see a wounded animal like that. Come on, Dook boy.'

'Don't you want some of the meat?' McGinn asked, knowing the village men would skin and divide up the carcase.

'No, sir. I want no part of it. Those guys were using number ten birdshot and seventy millimetre ball-trap shot, and in my book that's cruelty. That old hog was blinded in one eye for sure, and it was a very undignified way to go for a proud animal that don't do nobody any harm in this world unless he's wounded by man.'

Tex the hunter strolled away, gun swaying at his hip, followed by his faithful bird-dog, up the hill towards the church.

There would be squabbling over who had a leg and who had ribs, and they did not wait to hear it. 'You must be tired, Rupert,' McGinn said.

'No, I'm going to the *fête* tonight with Laurent and his parents. Nobody sleeps here during the *fête*. Manouche is great, isn't he? He must like his cats.'

'Yes, he likes his cats as much as Tex loves his dog. Men who fish and hunt often like animals more than those with pampered pets. They understand the cycle of nature. All year long the game birds eat the farmers' grapes, and then the farmers eat the birds in the hunting season. Tex only used the Schmeiser on that *sanglier* to put him out of his misery. The regulations on fishing and hunting have to be respected, as they're made to protect wildlife as well.'

'I'd like to go hunting with Tex some day.'

'You will, some day when you are older and you pass the hunting exam.'

Returning very late from their dinner date, the *fête* had ended earlier than the previous night as people were now beginning to get tired after three nights of feasting and dancing. As they passed the place where the ham was hanging in the tree, McGinn thought he saw a figure in the gloom.

'Did my eyes deceive me,' he said to Carolyn when they were in the house, 'or did I see a little man with a shotgun lurking near that ham? It looked like *Monsieur le garde-champêtre* to me.'

'Do you suppose someone would try to steal it?'

'Or borrow a ladder and measure it.' McGinn thought of the village ladder attached to the wall near the *Mairie*, and of Manouche and his confidence that he was going to win the ham. An enormous mountain ham was expensive and often given as first prize in Loto or Tombola contests in the villages. A grape picker would have to work a full week to earn enough to buy one.

'It's been an exciting day - and tiring,' Carolyn said.

'Do you know we fished in four rivers today and caught half a dozen varieties of fish? I reckon it would be possible to take the car and swim in five lakes and five rivers in one day. We'll do it some day soon, just for the fun of it. And some day soon we'll swim in two seas in one day.'

'Two seas?'

'A quick dip in the Med at Agde, then a five-hour drive to Bayonne and jump into the Atlantic waves.'

'That wine must have been strong.'

'We'll do it, just wait and see.'

On the final day of the village *fête,* there were bleary eyes and the odd stifled yawn. Soon there would be a distant sound like a cats' choir or an intoxicated orchestra tuning up as the youth of the village with a variety of instruments knocked on doors, entered, and tortured the occupants until they made a contribution to the festivities. McGinn packed the picnic baskets, put wine in the *glacier*, and prepared to make a run for it, pausing briefly to pass a contribution through the car window to a member of the 'orchestra'.

On the terrace of the café where they were to meet Patrice and his fiancée Fréderique, there was a surprise: the plasterer Jean-Paul had returned from the North and was sitting in front of three empty *demi* glasses and nursing a fourth.

'I had a piece of incredible luck,' he said. 'I had to change trains in

Toulouse, bought a beer from the trolley on the platform and left my wallet with a month's wages in it - on the trolley. I telephoned the station-master from Beziers and he said it had been handed in to his office and he would put it on the next train for me.'

'So you're celebrating,' McGinn said.

'Have a look in the basket inside the door of the bar,' said J-P, pointing to the corner of the doorway.

The basket contained a kilo jar of Dijon mustard, a large parcel from Monsieur Perez the butcher containing the portions of two rabbits ready for grilling, a quarter of a kilo of Roquefort cheese and slices of cut ham.

'*Lapin a la moutarde*,' said J-P as Patrice and Freddy arrived bearing picnic baskets and a *glacier*.

'One quick *"apéro"* and we're off,' said Patrice.

The picnic place was on the River Mare, near an ancient and ruined watermill within sight of the *Pont du Diable*. Within minutes of arriving, Rupert was snorkelling in the clear water watching the fish which were facing upstream and feeding. They were joined by a sculptor friend, Jomy, and his wife Marie-Claude from the nearby village and Patrice set about building a fire to grill the rabbit which Freddy was smothering with the Dijon mustard. Patrice opened a basket and took out a heap of sticks.

'What are the sticks?' Carolyn asked him.

'Apple wood. You get the flavour in the rabbit.'

Carolyn glanced at McGinn.

'The French,' he said. 'Only the French would bring their own apple wood to a picnic.'

'The flavour is everything,' said Patrice. 'I'll tell you a little story about that: Freddy and I were in a roadside restaurant on the cherry run near the Orb Valley and they had five flavours of *sorbet* in five compartments of the dishes. They gave us five spoons each so that we would not mix the flavours.'

'I'll tell you a story,' McGinn said, 'about a friend of mine who was with someone in a restaurant in Paris who complained about the flavour of the meat. The chef came out brandishing a meat cleaver. "What do you English know about cooking?" he shouted. "There's nothing wrong with that meat. You burn your meat to a cinder like you did *Jeanne d'Arc* - and furthermore your bloody Christmas puddings do *not* last for ten years."'

Jean-Paul took control of the cooking, smothering each morsel of rabbit with the Dijon mustard and placing the pieces on the grill. It would be a while before the fire was right for cooking, so they explored a tunnel that led under a rich man's country house nearby. The tunnel was half-filled with fine sand, silted up from the river when it was high in winter, and they had to lie flat and shuffle forward, heads low to avoid the ancient stones of the curved roof. The journey was worth it for beyond lay a placid pool, deep and calm, a perfect place for swimming or for fishing, a place to note for future fishing trips in the early morning when it was cool.

They had taken to refer to the sun as 'the enemy' for now the temperature was reaching its highest point of the year and it would stay that way until the grape harvest in September.

If there was work to be done on the land, spraying *bordelaise* if there were traces of the yellow blight on the leaves, or cutting passages through the spreading tentacles of vine forming barriers through the rows, the farmers took their tractors out at five a.m. and came home at eleven a.m., staying indoors until they returned for further work in the cool of the evening.

There was shade beneath the bridge or cast from the water-mill when they ate at midday. In the high summer there was not much shade by the lakes, but there was always a breeze off the sea-shore and good shade by the rivers. The afternoon was drowsy. Bees moved slowly from stamen to stamen of the wild flowers that grew on the banks of the river and swifts darted upstream, beaks open to catch the midges. High overhead, a skylark fluttered and sang, background music to the trickling shushing of water over pebbles on the river bank. Later, swimming in the river the water was cool, and it was possible to snorkel and catch a glimpse of a flashing Fario trout or the bull's head *Cabot*, known as Miller's thumb, feeding in the current. Evening brought the hatch of flies and the brown trout rose to take them upstream, with the rings spreading on the surface of the water after the fish plopped back in again, lazily feeding until the sun went down and it would be time for the night animals, hedgehog, fox and badger, to come out to play.

At an ancient bar they stopped for drinks, a bar that had not changed since 1918, with marble top tables, a sawdust on plank floor and faded posters and pictures on the wall, served by a friendly lady who remembered them from previous visits.

In the village where they had been invited for supper, the terrace where we were to eat overlooked a courtyard and there were other diners on other terraces which faced each other. There was some kind of tension in the air of the narrow streets and the alleyways and courtyards which retained the captured heat of the summer's day, in the village where once bandits from the hills had hidden and in the past there had been fights and gun battles, where on each corner of the thousand-year-old church stone animals warded off demons and evil spirits, and one of them, a snarling dog, displaying a human male erection where its natural organs should have been.

Suddenly, the church bell rang out, startlingly, sending a flock of linnets rising from a plane tree, sending its quavering notes through the streets of the Litany and the Rosary and over the ancient ramparts and the distant hills. There followed a faint clap of thunder from many miles away.

'*Orage*,' said Patrice, forecasting a rainstorm.

'Not before midnight,' said Jean-Paul the countryman from the Aveyron. 'It will clear the air, and the farmers need it for their grapes, but we won't be able to fish the streams for a week afterwards.'

'I'd like to have that house where we crawled through the tunnel,' said Patrice. 'It must be nice to be rich. The owner has spent a fortune on it.'

'But he scarcely ever goes there,' said Jean-Paul. 'Maybe four weeks in summer, that's all. All he ever sees is a balance sheet, the stock exchange report, the back of his chauffeur's head. Do you think he ever sees a sunrise or sunset?'

'You sound like André Gide,' McGinn said, 'who said there's no worse sight in the world than a busy man.'

'That's right. He's too busy to see a tree or a flower or a bird in flight, or his own house on the river, where we can go any time we like. *He's not rich. We're rich.*'

'Enough philosophising,' said Fréderique, the practical Parisienne, beating the mayonnaise in a bowl, one of her specialities. '*A table, s'il vous plaît.*'

147

They sat around the table on the terrace where moths were beginning to gather around the wall lamp. Across the courtyard the Marti family had already eaten. Monsieur Marti would be up at first light and in the fields by five a.m. On the terrace opposite, the Deloffre family were about to sit down with their *'apéros'* in their hands, laughing and chatting and sharpening their appetites.

'It's very public here,' said Carolyn. 'It's like living in other people's houses.'

'Yes - a close-knit community,' said Fréderique.

'This is where Neighbourhood Watch was invented,' McGinn said, and the French looked puzzled until Carolyn explained.

'Luckily there's not much crime here - not yet,' said Fréderique, beating eggs in a bowl and adding a touch of fresh cream to make an *omelette aux cèpes.*

'My wallet was returned to me,' said Jean-Paul, 'and in this village two Paris friends on holiday last year dropped a wallet containing all their holiday money and it was handed in by a customer and given to Denis and Jo.'

'I didn't dare tell Carolyn this,' McGinn said, 'but the other night I left the car keys and a five hundred franc note on the seat of the car with an open window. Everyone who went to the *fête* must have seen the money, and anyone could have taken it, but they didn't.'

'Old age pensioners buy grapes in the shops here,' said Carolyn. 'They're surrounded by fields of them but they don't take them because it would be stealing.'

'It'll all change,' said McGinn the cynic.

'I have heard, though,' he added, 'that it is not unknown for some people to help themselves to asparagus.'

'Ah, yes, true,' said Patrice. 'I know one or two people who have an asparagus knife in the car boot tool box.'

'If you plant asparagus around here you're asking for trouble,' said Jean-Paul, 'unless the bedroom window overlooks the field and you invest in floodlights or a rifle with telescopic night sights.'

Monsieur Marti came back onto his terrace in a dressing gown. The rest of the family had gone inside the house.

'And not too much noise tonight,' he shouted across at the Deloffres opposite, whose chatting and gaiety came to a sudden halt.

'Oh, no. It's about to start again,' said Fréderique.

'Some people,' shouted Monsieur Marti, 'have to work.'

'Shut up,' called Bernard, the Deloffre family teenager.

'You shut up,' his father said. 'Ignore the old fool.'

'He's annoyed,' said Patrice, 'because someone - I'm not sure who but he's so near I could spit on him - wrote on the wall of Marti's house: THE HOUSE OF THE OLD BASTARD in letters a metre high. It cost him two thousand francs to have the walls re-painted.'

'So that's how you bought the Deux Chevaux,' said Jean-Paul.'

Patrice laughed. 'It wasn't me,' he said. 'I suspect his initials are Bernard Deloffre.'

'Everyone's too close together here,' said Carolyn, 'and I imagine nerves get more frayed as a heat-wave starts.'

'Too true,' said Fréderique. 'Did you hear about Claudine sunbathing in the nude in her garden, complaining to the *Mairie* that Monsieur Gonzales is a *voyeur* and peeps at her from behind his curtains?'

'What does she expect?' Carolyn said.

'They made him close his shutters permanently, anyway. He's not allowed to look out of his own windows.'

'Her ex-husband tells a different story,' said Jean-Paul. 'He claims Gonzales complained to the *Mairie* that his view was being ruined by a big white body in the garden below and he was forced to close his shutters against the horrible sight.'

'Oh, he would say that. That's because he's still in love with her,' said Fréderique.

'You would say that,' said Patrice, 'because you're a woman...'

'STOP THAT NOISE,' came a shout from Monsieur Marti's bedroom window on the terrace, trying to drown the sound of music from young Bernard's selection from the latest pop-video-reggae-metal-band tapes he had collected.

'SHUT YOUR BIG GOB,' called Bernard.

'Watch out, it's starting again,' said Fréderique.

'Fasten your safety belts. Take your backward-facing seats for the Marti-Deloffre show. Pass the cotton wool.'

'WHO SAID THAT?' Monsieur Marti was out on his terrace, dressing gown flapping.

'Hazard a guess,' shouted Bernard, or words to that effect.

'Be quiet,' said Monsieur Deloffre, pushing his son in the chest and trying to keep the peace at least until they had finished the cheese course.

'You young layabout cretin,' shouted Monsieur Marti.

'Social Security scrounger, living off the backs of working farmers. Why don't you get a job?'

'I can't, you old idiot, haven't you seen the unemployment figures? There's no jobs for young people.'

'Join the Army.'

'OK, I will, and when they give me a gun I'll shoot you.'

CRASH. A potted geranium, thrown by Monsieur Marti landed on the Deloffre's terrace, missing the music lover by fifty centimetres. Bernard's father came storming out of the room onto the terrace in a rage, looked at the Provençal ochre tiles bestrewn with black potting earth and the tattered remnants of the geranium, shook his fist at the disappearing back of Monsieur Marti's dressing gown and yelled: 'You old fool - you could have killed my son.' He was joined by Madame Deloffre on the terrace, armed with a broom, her house-proud demeanour shattered by the wreckage on her normally spotless terrace.

'I'll show him,' said Deloffre, picking up a plant pot containing a deep purple petunia and hurling it across the divide so that it crashed through Monsieur Marti's window.

'My petunia,' sobbed Madame Deloffre.

'Programmes, chocolates, ices, cigarettes,' said Fréderique, leaning on the balustrade of the terrace to watch the show, eyes bright with humour in her beautiful pixie face.

'Do you want another?' yelled Monsieur Deloffre, picking up the potted begonia.

'Not the begonia,' shouted Madame Deloffre, trying to snatch the pot out of his hand. Suddenly she let a shrill scream and ran inside the house, followed by a scattering of chairs and dishes from the table as young Bernard tried to beat his father in the race to take cover, and the potted begonia slipped from Monsieur Deloffre's hand as he pushed Bernard aside and managed to squeeze through the terrace door first, just behind his hysterical wife.

Monsieur Marti stood on the terrace loading up a 12-bore shotgun.

'*Nom de Dieu*, he's got a gun,' said Fréderique, hastily backing away from the balustrade.

'*Merde*,' said Jean-Paul. 'This is getting serious.'

BANG. The first barrel went off, blasting two petunias and a cactus off the terrace wall and splattering earth and flowers and fireclay over the terrace, some of the pellets bouncing off the thick glass windows.

BANG. The second barrel followed immediately, the spread shot taking another cactus and a begonia neatly off the low wall and scattering their remnants over the remains of the cheese course on the table. Screams and sobs came from within the Deloffre household, mingled with shouts and curses as Monsieur Deloffre's fear turned to rage.

Monsieur Marti, clearly a crack shot at the *ball-trap* in his day, neatly picked up the discarded *chevrotine* shells and disappeared inside his house.

'I don't believe this,' said Carolyn. 'It's the Wild West here,' she added in a whisper as Monsieur Deloffre and son Bernard appeared on their terrace, each brandishing an under-and-over twelve gauge pump action shotgun and sporting bandoliers of cartridges.

'Bit early for the hunting season, isn't it?' McGinn asked, trying to be casual, but his French friends were disturbed, quickly picking up their lighters and cigarettes and bottles of wine to take indoors.

'Come on, quickly, let's go,' said Fréderique.

'Any minute now the Gendarmes will be here,' said Jean-Paul. Somebody is bound to have telephoned after the first shot. There's going to be questions, statements, and some people are going to spend the night in the cells...'

'Run,' said Patrice, 'quick, quick, all go home.'

The gun battle started in earnest as they fled down the stairs and towards the parked cars near the church, the pellets smashing into the shutters which Monsieur Marti had had the foresight to close before reaching for his gun.

'See you at Alignan on Friday,' called Fréderique as they started the motors which failed to drown out the sound of bombardment from the courtyard. They separated after the fountain, Patrice and Jean-Paul driving towards the oncoming Black Maria, siren flashing and alarm sounding, just as J-P had predicted, as Carolyn drove right at the crossroads and onto the country road.

'I told you it was the Wild West down here,' McGinn said as he closed the front door. 'Road signs shot up, wild boar slaughtered before our eyes, supper interrupted by the battle of the OK Corral.'

'My friends were right. They said if I lived with you I'd never be bored.'

'The cops will want statements from all the neighbours and witnesses. Marti and Deloffre will reach for their lawyers, they'll both be bound over to keep the peace by the judge when the court case comes up, and the lawyers, gunsmiths and flower sellers will be richer. There won't be much sleep for either Marti or Deloffre tonight.'

'Are you tired?'

'Not tired. I think it's battle fatigue.'

Carolyn laughed. 'I'll be back in a minute,' McGinn said, 'I'm just going down to the *Mairie*. The councillors will be clearing up after the fête.'

'What's so interesting about that?'

'I want to know who won that ham.'

The long tables had been cleared of debris from the meal and stacked against the wall of the school ready for storing in the morning. Many black plastic sacks of rubbish lay in readiness for the *garde-champêtre* with his tractor and trailer. The councillors nibbled on the remains of the cutlets and cheese and cake, a perquisite for their tasks.

'Who won the ham?' McGinn asked a neighbour.

'He wasn't from these parts.'

'What did he look like?'

'He looked like a praying mantis with a blonde wig.'

'Or a race-horse with blonde curls,' said another councillor, both of them clearly annoyed that the prize had gone outside the village.

'That's Manouche,' McGinn said.

'He certainly looked as if he needed a feed off that ham,' said the neighbour. 'If they audition for a film about a famine, he'll certainly get a part in it.'

'How did the *fête* go, anyway?'

'Not good.'

'Better than last year, anyway.'

They laughed, but the laughter was a little forced. The previous year the so-called 'treasurer' had run off with all the money in the coffers to pay for the brasucade and the orchestra and provide the beer and food for visitors. At first it was thought that he'd gone to Monte Carlo, but he had not been that ambitious. There was a Casino in Montpellier. He returned to his shocked wife and children and the opprobrium of the village, but grateful that not a single person had talked, so the police were not involved. There was a rumour that he had promised to pay back every franc before the year 2050.

'We're going to have another *fête* later to re-coup the cost of the orchestra,' said the neighbour.

Every year they said that. They never had enough to pay the cost of the orchestra, so there was debt at the end of every *fête*, yet the generous tradition of a free meal for everyone in the village on *Quatorze Juillet* continued.

The village that *had* cracked the secret of making a profit out of the *fête* was the one Frédérique had invited them to on Friday night. Very simply, they had one *every* Friday night. Someone on the council must have wanted to dispense with the wine lake, and came up with the idea of *giving it away* to all the campers on the village camp site during the summer, but, naturally, throwing in a snack of mussels in white wine, sausages and pork chops and kebabs or *brochette*, cheese, cake for the children and thrusting a litre of red and a litre of *rosé* at everyone in sight. It became so popular over the years that they started to make a small charge and issue tickets for the queues that formed early in the evening. Word spread that it was possible for grandfather, grandmother, mother, father, three children and assorted aunts to have a wonderful evening's dancing and feasting in the open air for the price of a *couchette* on the Beziers-Paris train.

The profit came from opening a champagne bar and a beer bar, for, having eaten and drunk and danced for next to nothing and with a pocket full of holiday money, what better than a bottle or two of champagne or Blanquette de Limoux to round off a superb evening?

The sound of merry-making met them halfway up the hill and serenaded them through rows of cars on every road leading into the village and in the packed car park of the Co-operative. Four hundred laughing, cheering, jumping, singing, jostling, shuffling, shouting people crammed the huge concrete dance floor, high as kites and loving every minute of it. Grandfathers dancing with six-year-olds, teenagers with grandmothers, lovers clutching each other, men dancing with their wives and other men's wives; gendarmes danced with secretaries, rugbymen with lady cashiers, tilers with typists, bank clerks with bakers...

They looked into the sea of faces, bobbing and jostling and weaving, trying to spot familiar ones from other villages. Panique was dancing, taking up the space of three others with his barn-door-width shoulders. Spider Smith was dancing with his attractive Indonesian wife, wearing a lemon coloured shirt and bottle-green trousers. With his red, cracked capillary face, he resembled a set of traffic lights. Manouche was dancing with Brigitte, the wife of Champagne Jock, while he sat near the beer bar nursing a 'foetus' of Johnny Walker whisky. Jean-Paul, who did not dance, stood at the centre of a thirsty circle at the beer bar and bought round after round of drinks for everyone in sight, including the three bartenders. Even the Sheriff was dancing with one of the local girls, relaxing after a hard day persecuting motorists. Georges Galette danced, surprisingly well for a man with such a Kronenbourg muscle, with his wife. Looking at Georges made everyone think of menus, dozens and dozens of menus that he must have sampled in his time.

This was the end of July crowd, with quite a few from Paris as the French now staggered their holidays over half of July and half of September as opposed to the old rigid August-only vacation, but the real crowd from Paris had not yet arrived. There were campers from various countries, mainly Holland, Belgium and England, a smattering of Germans and Scandinavians, and many relatives of local families visiting the region.

Champagne Jock waved and they joined him at the trestle table.

'Will ye just look at that lot there,' he said, pointing at the heaving dance-floor. 'It makes me weak to look at them. That Manouche is tryin' to get off wi' ma missus. He just tried to sell me a ham.'

'How much?' Carolyn asked.

'Too bloody much. I offered him eight bottles of champagne for it, but he wants cash. He says he's going to start a snail farm and make a fortune. He says all you need is a few old drain pipes and tin chimneys and the snails multiply like rabbits.'

The music stopped and the crowds left the dance-floor. Suddenly all the chairs were taken and there was lots of hand-shaking and cheek-kissing in greeting.

Curious about the ham, McGinn took Manouche aside.

'How did you manage to win the ham?' he asked.

'Ah.'

'I'm sworn to secrecy.'

'Promise?'

'Promise.'

'With the fishing rod. I knew that the ham was roughly placed six metres off the ground and I have a six-metre fishing rod, the one you saw me using in the river. At night I put the rod up to the ham and with a tape measure took the distance from the bottom of the rod to the road. It was only three centimetres. So I bet six metres two, six metres three, and six metres four centimetres, and with three bets I won it.'

'But they put a guard on it.'

'Ah, yes - after I had measured it. You see I suspected someone else might try to measure it, so I placed the *garde-champêtre's* ladder against the base of the tree so that they would *suspect* someone was about to try it. It worked, and they guarded the stable after the horse had left.'

'When's the next fishing trip?'

'Oh, I'm going to leave it until the Paris crowd come down in August. I'm planning to start a snail farm. I need to make some money here and snail-farming is the latest thing.'

Spider Smith joined the group and said he had heard that Manouche was starting a snail farm. 'Snails, I dunno,' said Spider. 'Like chewing a condom, I always think. And all that preparation. Too much bloody work for my likin'.'

Manouche, asking what Spider had said, laughed and then smiled that smug smile. 'Nothing to it,' he said. 'You simply guard the snails for eight to ten days in thyme and rosemary, then let them dégorge themselves in salted water and vinegar. You wash them in lots of water, then boil them for five minutes in salted water, take the snails out, boil the shells in salted water then dry them. Now you are ready to cook them. Garlic chopped fine, parsley, salt and pepper, butter, a bit in the shell, the snail pushed in, the hole filled up, and fifteen minutes in the hot oven - *eh voila! Les Escargots a la bourguignonne.'*

'I got about half of that,' said Spider, 'and that's still too much work. Anyway, I prefer the English method. What they do down in Devon is first they stampede them, then they smother 'em with a pillow to bring out the flavour. If that don't work, they throw red pepper at them and when they come out to sneeze, they lasso them.'

'What you say?' Manouche was puzzled.

'He's just joking, Manouche, winding you up,' said Jock. 'You go ahead and do your snail farm. Come to think of it, it sounds like a nice *leisurely* way tae make a living.' He looked hard at his wife Brigitte when he stressed the word. 'There's none of this nonsense about gettin' oot o' bed at five in the mornin' an' snaggin' swede an all that. No frozen mitts and achin' back. No *perspirin'*.'

'Vell, vy don' you go in business wiz eem?' cried Brigitte, glaring at Jock. ''Ow you call it in English - a sleeping partner. You would like zat. You know 'ees so lazee 'ee hask me to wind 'ees watch for 'eem.'

'Will ye listen tae that? Here ah am, wearin' ma brain tae the bone tryin' tae think up schemes tae to get some readies, an' all ah get is insults...'

The orchestra struck up again and the dance floor was filled within five minutes.

Manouche said: 'We must have a *mechoui* when the Paris crowd arrive. If everybody contributes, I can order a sheep from a farmer who comes down here from the Aveyron once a week to deliver. We could have it in the old *distillerie* garden.'

'How many people?' Carolyn asked.

'Between twenty-five and thirty-five,' said Manouche.

'Gilles and his new girl friend are coming down from Brittany, with Yvon and his new girl friend, that's four, then Panique and Madame, J-P., Freddy, Patrice, Jeanne-Pierre and a couple of majorettes, Georges Galette and Madame, Alfie, Tom Plumb, Ginger, Dave, Martine and Bash...'

'*Moment*,' said Manouche. 'We'd better make it two sheep. With the gang here, that's more than twenty-five and we have not yet counted the Paris people. It's no problem, I get a discount for ordering two.'

'Of course, there'll be Denis and Jo, and Patrick and Bernadette, his parents, her parents, Maddo, Zush, Frank, Jean-Jacques...'

'Hey, hey. If this goes on it will have to be *three* sheep...'

'We'll make out a list and let you know in good time, Manouche,' said Carolyn. 'Not all of them will be able to turn up on the night. I'm sure two sheep will be enough.'

'What about wine?' McGinn asked.

'Oh, a hundred litres should be enough,' said Manouche. 'I can get a discount from the Co-op...'

'What about some champagne?' Jock asked.

'Too expensive,' said Manouche.

'Ah can let ye have it fer half price.'

'Here - I'll buy the champagne,' said Spider. 'How many bottles can you let me have at half price, then?'

'Twenty.'

'OK, I'll buy them.'

'That's a deal, Spider.'

'I'm goin' to be flush soon anyway, cos I'm letting my new gaff to some tourists from Holland and I'm going to camp out in "bis" next door. It's no hardship to me. I've kipped in enough *vendangeurs'* pads to make it seem 'ome from 'ome. I remember that first year I kipped in Delmas's gaff. I was so hungover I couldn't get to work, but I didn't know he locked the door before he went to the fields. When I crept down that ladder at ten o'clock I found I'd been locked in.'

'You could have shouted for help,' Carolyn said. 'The shop is just opposite. One of the customers would have heard you.'

'Oh, I did, but not very loud. You see there was a twenty litre drum of wine by the door and a clean empty glass. I spent a lovely morning. From time to time I called "h-e-l-p".' Spider croaked the word in a hoarse whisper. 'Not too loud of course, in case someone heard me. "H-e-l-p, h-e-l-p",' he whispered.

The sound of the orchestra drowned the laughter as everyone stamped their feet and sang the words of a popular song, usually played towards the end of the evening. Some of the older people and the young children were drifting away now and soon the traffic jam would start in the narrow streets.

'Look out - trouble,' said Patrice.

'Where - what?' said Fréderique.

'Marie-Lise. And she has just seen her husband, and he's waving a five hundred franc note under the barman's nose.'

'That's the end of his alcoholiday,' said Carolyn.

'She'll drag him back up north to finish building that house,' said Patrice.

Like a little net-ball player, Marie-Lise dodged through the crowd of Jean-Paul's admirers, and leapt up and neatly snatched the 500 franc note from his fingers before the barman could get to it.

'My house-keeping money,' she cried, making for Jean-Paul to put a half-Nelson on him, but he wriggled away as his drinking cronies stepped back, embarrassed by the domestic squabble. Mentally tossing a coin and finding discretion to be more advisable than valour, he allowed her to grip his sleeve and conduct him towards the exit of the little park where the weekly *fête* took place.

'He'll miss the *mechoui*,' said Patrice.

'Want to make a bet?' asked Fréderique.

'No.'

'He'll be back in a week,' she said.

'I think you're right.'

More of the crowd of dancers were drifting away now towards their cars, and it was time to make a break for it before the lanes became littered with the glass from head-on collisions between rear-view mirrors as no-one gave way, or the sound of crunching fenders as cars were eased out of narrow parking places or reversed slowly into low walls or neighbouring cars, or into the conveniently placed ditches which lined every road and vineyard for miles around.

Next day there was a crisis in the village in the morning, followed by one in the afternoon, followed by a children's party, followed by the boys' *petanque* match, to be administered by fond fathers looking upon their sons as future champions.

Throwing back the curtains at 7 a.m. with the usual cry of 'Tralaaaa' to herald the sun which crashed through those windows on three hundred and twenty days a year, the first crisis came when the electric kettle failed to work. An electricity cut, or strike or breakdown. Neighbours were out in the street checking with each other. Yes, it had affected everyone. It was a mistake to panic, for no matter whether it was a strike, a breakdown or a cut for repair work to be carried out, all would be well inside 24 hours. A strike would be broken, wages settled, men back to work, or repairs would go on by arc-light through the night, or the *garde-champêtre* would announce the length of the temporary cut to assuage the populace. One thing was sure - there would be plenty of current within 24 hours, for that was when the FOOD IN THE DEEP FREEZE CHESTS STARTED TO GO OFF! All those rabbits shot with .22 rifles and frozen, all those chops bought cheap in supermarket sales, all those stuffed tomatoes and aubergines the wives had made from garden produce, the ice cream, the cake, the frozen asparagus and strawberries, the cuts of the unfortunate *sanglier* which had foolishly run into the village streets, the trout in M. Marcel's fridge freezer... all had to be saved in time. This was France, after all. If that electricity was not back in time, insurance companies would be contacted, estimates made of the value of the contents of the *congelateur*, and the bill would go to *Electricité de France*.

By midday the current was back on, but the postman's letter for Napoleon and Josefine caused the next crisis. They were knocking on the door. Could Monsieur McGinn help? The tourist lady who had danced with all the village men and caused such a scandal among the wives had paid for a bottle of butane gas with an English Sterling cheque, claiming it was the end of her holiday and she had run out of francs. The bank had charged as much for changing the money as the price of the bottle of gas. Josefine had suffered a mild heart attack when she had seen the bank charges. Napoleon himself had thought he had a heart murmur as he administered coffee and aspirin to his stricken helpmeet. Could Monsieur McGinn write to the lady and ask her to make good the deficiency in their income as a result of the avarice of the French banks in making these extortionate charges?

Here was a chance to torture them, to worry to distraction these beheaders of jelly-babies. Of course he could write, but who would pay for the stamp? And the writing paper and the ink. Yes, yes, they would pay for the stamp... but... with worried frowns they asked how much the ink and paper would cost and for several seconds McGinn contemplated with an anxious frown this enormous outlay until he put them out of their misery by paying their bank charges and assuring them he would collect it from the lady tourist personally and they had no further need to worry. Their petty meanness was not unusual; each month an American - Texan author Max Crawford in Pézenas - put his rent cheque in an envelope for his landlady. Next day, she always gave him back the envelope - to be used again.

With Rupert in tow, he then went to get his *petanque* licence. Men and boys - especially boys - had to be licensed to play this highly dangerous sport. Boys who would risk death by drowning while ducking for apples would think nothing of clonking one of their mates with a heavy metal *boule* to become *petanque* champion.

The proud bearer of his licence, Rupert went off to the children's party, carrying a book Carolyn had bought as a present.

The children's party, given for the birthday of little Jean-Jacques, the underwater swimmer, aged nine, lasted for three hours, for parents were still tolerant of the children who were only two weeks into the eight weeks' summer holiday and nerves were not yet frayed. On his return, stuffed with cakes and biscuits, Rupert announced that he would give supper a miss that night. 'Did Jean-Jacques get some nice presents?' Carolyn asked him.

'He liked my book, but it was very strange, a bit embarrassing really, because all the other kids took him their broken toys: but he said it was all right, all the kids do that here.'

There was a rumble of thunder in the distance, the expected *orage* or electric storm would come soon, and the farmers were wanting it. 'Are you sure you want to take the Mobylette?' Carolyn asked McGinn.

'I'll risk it. It's not far and we need something for supper even if Master Rupert is full of jelly and cream cakes.'

It was a mistake. An electric storm in South West France has to be experienced to be believed: great flashes of white lightning zig-zagging across the sky and flashing like a million neon lights behind black clouds in the distance, then coming closer with the thunder cracking overhead and the lightning bouncing off the road. At a garage they advised: 'Don't try and get back to your village tonight. The road will be under water.'

McGinn fastened the shopping tightly into the wire basket and put on the crash helmet, determined to reach the safety of a nice warm bed rather than spend the night on someone's couch, and also knowing there were jobs to be done: every electric plug taken out of its socket, the TV aerial wire detached from the set, the telephone plugs removed from their sockets. The lightning had been known to put phones out of order and blow up TV sets.

In the distance the Chateau de Cassan stood out against the flash of lightning like Frankenstein's castle with its turrets and folly and pigeon houses. Once an orphanage for black boys from Reunion it was now a circus school. The road that ran alongside descends into a valley and was running with black water and the rain hit McGinn's face like a hundred pinpricks, but he had to get across the valley and up the other side by Cristobal's farm, where the *garagiste* had heard the road was bad. The lightning hit the road fifty yards ahead of the *moped*, and the river Thongue was already in flood beneath the brick bridge that spanned it. The *garagiste* had heard correctly and there was yellow clay on the road by the farm, swept down from the broken bankside. There was a flood of rushing water on the road, building up the clay banks in the centre and the bike skidded sideways several times. It was better to ride with the feet off the pedals for balance and in case the bike slid from under as the tyres slipped on the clay. Suddenly the ground became clear of flooding water, and, dodging potholes but with the lightning still dangerously close, he made the safety of the house.

'There is an old saying: "Never say no to an experience",' he said to Carolyn, taking off the dripping helmet. 'But that is one to say "no" to: a *moped* ride through an *orage* in the Herault.'

Only three unplugged TV sets were destroyed by the lightning in the village, and the air was clear and the morning cooler and calmer as the repair man inspected the neighbours' sets and gave estimates for the insurance companies. There was talk of a plastic greenhouse, twenty-five metres long, six metres wide and five metres high which had been lifted by the wind and taken *eight kilometres* to land in Magalas. A couple in another village, elderly farm people, had had their roof crash down in the bedroom and were rescued by neighbours.

After the *orage* the air would be clear and the weather boiling hot. The rivers would be in flood and the lakes disturbed. This was a good day to go to the beach. The sea would be calm after the storm and there would be the usual breeze off the shore. At Rochelongue it was possible to walk over a beach made entirely of sea-shells, enter the water, gather enough mussels and sea urchins, and have lunch from the bounty of the sea by adding a bottle of white wine and a *baguette*. At Tamarissière, it was possible to find the scallops called St Jacques, or have a *pan bagnat*, the delicious Mediterranean sandwich in a bun containing what amounted to a *salade Nicoise*: lettuce, tomatoes, olives, anchovies, and hard-boiled egg, from Claudine's beach bar at Farinette, accompanied, naturally, by a cold bottle of beer.

Then there were the great family beaches of Valras and Grau d'Agde and Marseillan, where local families took their own sunshades and beach chairs and *glaciers* of wine and soft drinks, and picnicked on the beaches which were unspoiled by commercialism.

The day was so hot that three hours on any beach was enough, although Rupert, like most children, would have played happily all day until he was well cooked.

Back in the village he began to worry because Midge the cat had not returned after the storm. Food he had put out for him had not been eaten, even though he had ready access through the cat-hole in the original ancient barn door.

'Do you think he was killed by lightning?' Rupert asked.

'Very unlikely. He probably got scared and is hiding somewhere. He'll be back, don't worry.'

Midge the cat, once a fluffy ball of kittenhood called Mouche, had grown into a fighting Tom, with scarred nose and half-torn ear from fights in the night streets of the village over the local cat talent, but McGinn feared that this battle-bruised warrior might be gone for ever, killed, perhaps, by curiosity. The local farmers ordered gin-traps from wholesalers' catalogues in the same way their wives ordered dresses. The gin-traps were set around chicken houses or *pigeonniers* against weasel, stoat, fox, badgers looking for eggs - or marauding cats and dogs. Where food was concerned, theft was theft, and there was no sentimentality. Unfortunately, when the farmers were busy with the sulphating machines, as they always were after rain when the ground hardened sufficiently to use the tractor, they might not visit the outlying livestock pens for several days...

When Rupert had arrived, McGinn had explained that this was still wild countryside in the South West, where snakes and eagles and badgers, foxes, and wild boar roamed and where scorpions lurked under stones, and giant bees were dangerous if they stung you on the tongue or throat or attacked in a confined space. Although there were no vipers - the nearest were in the Aveyron, an hour's drive away - it had been known for *vendangeurs* to be nipped by a scorpion and suffer a sick headache for an hour or two, but they were not lethal.

Visitors from Holland and England or a high-rise in Berlin found it hard to believe there were wild boar roaming in the valley of the butterflies just below the village, leaving their spoor on the clay path after rain, coming out to feed at night in ancient orchards where the irresistible smell of windfall ripe apples tempted them from the *maquis* and the scrubland where they hid.

There was a tapping on the window. They looked and saw a beautiful sight - a hoopoe, with its orange plumage and crest and long curved shining beak battering on the window pane and looking from side to side, probably at its own reflection. McGinn opened the window, hoping it would come in, but it flew off. He closed the window and it returned and tapped again. This went on for ten minutes until it flew off to the valley below. To see a hoopoe so close up was a memorable sight. The window had to stay closed, however, against the ichneumon fly, a spider-hunting wasp which they had made the mistake of ignoring and allowing into the house. The insect, looking as if he had two bodies, returned time and again with minute pieces of soft clay from ponds and built a nest behind a tapestry, a solid clay ball, cleverly constructed with a dozen small compartments. Break open this ball and little spiders will run out. The ichneumon has laid its eggs in the living spiders, imprisoned in their cells, for the result of this horrific aspect of nature in the raw is that the icheumon's eggs will hatch out and feed off the living spider. The fly-screen in the South West of France is not just against house-flies and mosquitoes...

Then the 75 number plates began to appear and they knew that Paris was on holiday for the whole of August, and there would be merry-making for thirty days and dancing in the streets at the fêtes.

It was time to prepare the *mechoui*.

CHAPTER SEVEN

WHEN Midge the cat finally appeared he had two claws missing. He had certainly been caught in a *piege* or animal trap near a chicken pen, and although Manouche offered cures with herbs gypsy-style, he was taken to the vet, for proper claw amputation and the bill came to 400 francs.

'Four hundred francs? For a cat? You've got a gun, haven't you?' said old Monsieur Marcel the feather plucker with the watering-can. 'Anyone here would have given you another kitten.' But Midge was part of the family, and he padded around with his bandaged paw just waiting to get back into the fray with the other village Toms.

The two sheep for the *mechoui* were supplemented with twenty kilos of mussels, cooked in an enormous shallow iron dish and liberally sprinkled with white wine. Jean-Paul had managed to escape from the North and arrived bearing a whole Roquefort cheese and a whole mountain ham. Yves and Guillaume, two wine growers who had their own private brands of *eau de vie de marc*, provided the *digestifs*. This *marc* would soon disappear for ever in France, for it was made privately and the mothers of Yves and Guillaume held the licence to make it that would die with them. When the laws were changed to stop private distilling in the early fifties, when a glass of milk was called a 'Mendes-France' by Paris waiters, it was the beginning of the end for all the country people who distilled their own *marc* and prune, pear and apple liqueurs.

While the mussels were being eaten, half a dozen men wanted to get in on the act of roasting the two sheep, skewered onto bars through two timing clocks which were wound up with a key so that the spring would slowly turn the sheep as they were basted. When about to do a grill, McGinn had always found it advisable to ask: 'Is there a Frenchman here who knows about grilling?' and half a dozen would rush forward to demonstrate their skill, sprinkling handfuls of salt onto recalcitrant flames threatening to scorch the meat, prodding and testing and keeping the fire at the right temperature.

'Don't overcook that sheep,' a wag called out to them. 'It's not Joan of Arc you know.'

Manouche said: 'I thought someone was going to provide champagne for this *mechoui*. Spider Smith, wasn't it?'

Spider, hearing his name, moved closer to the group by the fire.

'I was keeping a bit quiet about that,' said Spider. 'It's a bit embarrassing, like. Champagne Jock won't be with us tonight, I'm afraid. 'e's in the slammer. Got his collar felt at the supermarket this mornin' walking out of the extra large goods exit with a suitcase full of champagne. What he was doin' you see was going in, filling a half price suitcase off the shelf with champagne, then wheeling it out and paying for the bargain price suitcase and selling the champers later - and the suitcase too, if you recollect his sales pitch. Been doin' it for months. They got smart and started opening suitcases at the cashiers desk.'

'Does his wife Brigitte know?'

'Does she know? It was her idea. She's advised him to say he did it for a bet, and if that doesn't work, plead guilty but temporarily insane, due to pressure of work, holiday intoxication and sun-stroke.'

'Hey, is there anything to drink around here,' called Jean-Paul, waving an empty glass. 'I know there's a dog called *Toujours Faim* - well, I'm called *Toujours Soif.*'

'Mister Always Thirsty's in a good mood,' Carolyn said.

'He's just heard his wife's divorcing him,' said Spider. 'But he'd better watch out. If 'e don't pay maintenance, she'll put the law onto him.'

Patflic came over to Patrice and said: 'The barber's shop tomorrow?' Patflic, or Patrick the *flic* was some kind of secret police operative in Paris and came on holiday every August when he allowed the local barber to crop his hair right off, down to the scalp, in the belief that this 'strengthened' the hair. Patrice usually joined him and they would sit on the café terrace, their heads like two bladders of lard, swapping anecdotes. It was generally assumed that Patflic's work involved checking up on Paris bars and tasting wine and beers to make sure they were up to scratch and not requiring analysis by the Weights and Measures inspectors, and he was so keen on his work that he even did it on his day off. On holiday he always had his head shaved and tried to get physically fit by jogging, swimming, fishing and hunting in readiness for the return to work.

'Trouble ahead...' someone said as a fierce argument broke out between Gilles, 'Le Pirate' and Panique the wrestler over who was to have the hot brains of the first sheep to be ready for the table. They each wielded implements and tools in readiness for the opening of the sheep's skull. Gilles had a hammer and chisel, and Panique held a saw and an axe.

'You can have the second lot,' shouted Panique.

'I'm hungry. I want the first lot,' shouted Gilles.

'I've been slaving over this fire for two hours,' shouted Panique. Gilles began to yell back at him and the French became so fast and furious it was hard to follow, and some of the English guests were mildly shocked at this display of savagery, a battle over hot sheep's brains by two gourmets.

'Compromise, compromise,' shouted Patflic. 'I'll have them.'

'Oh no you won't, Monsieur,' said Panique, getting to work with the saw. 'Chef's perquisites go to the chef.'

'And the assistant chef,' said Gilles. 'Fifty-fifty, OK?'

He offered his hand to Panique and there was an audible sigh of relief when the wrestler backed down and agreed to share.

More and more guests arrived at the old distillery where the *mechoui* was being held in the garden and helped themselves to plates of mussels while the chefs, having devoured their 'delicacy' were expertly carving the meat and serving it quickly to a queue of people holding plates already laden with salad.

Manouche was heard saying: '...an excellent *soupe de cresson*... Oh yes, just so long as there are no sheep in the region... you see...'

Jean-Paul was saying: 'Peace and quiet, that's what I'll wake up to in my little cabin in the vines. And I have a nightingale that sings especially for me, just outside my window. What more could a man want...?'

Spider Smith said: 'She's going to the *notaire* definitely, to complain about me. I can't understand what all the fuss is about. I haven't used the mixer for two weeks and still she rabbits on at me every time I walk out of the front door. And I've got my Dutch tourists arriving soon, a couple and three kids...'

Fréderique said: 'The meat's tough.'

Bash said: 'Isn't there any mint sauce?'

Martine was unloading fifty goat cheeses she had brought from a goat farm that had started in her village.

Patrice said: 'Always remove the Camembert from the paper and put it back in the box so that it can mature and ripen naturally. And when you cut the first triangle out, stand the box up so the cheese doesn't run out of the skin.'

Jean-Paul said: 'Camembert is a *summer* cheese, not a winter cheese... It must be allowed to run to maturity.'

Ginger said: 'Any redcurrant jelly?'

Tex Ranald said: 'Hot brains, huh? Could be Texas.'

Carolyn said: 'It's enough to turn one into a vegetarian.'

Manouche was saying: '...be a millionaire. Do you know how much they pay for snail's *eggs* in Paris and London now? It's like selling *caviar*, and a New York market is opening up. What with that and the grenache...'

Francois the Fingers said: 'What this party needs is fireworks - a few rockets going off and a few Roman candles.'

'What this party needs,' said Henry Catchpole, 'is some music. And some dancing. Put the music on, someone.'

Denis said: '*A l'entente cordiale*. Frogs and *Rosbifs*.'

The music started up and the dancing began and Panique and Gilles agreed to let Patflic have a taste of the brains from the second sheep, just so long as he didn't put the word around.

The party was by now in full swing, and Patflic looked around and said: 'Just think of it - at least ten more fêtes to go to during the holiday, and all the picnics, then another *mechoui* at the end. I'll need a holiday afterwards.'

The *mechoui* lasted until dawn was beginning to break in the sky, and there were rabbits in the headlights and hedgehogs scuttling off the road as McGinn and Carolyn drove home. The first ray of sun just touched the tops of the trees that bordered the valley of the butterflies and the dawn chorus filled the village as blue-tit, sparrow, blackbird, thrush, swifts, and swallows joined in to welcome the new day.

'Poor old champagne Jock in dungeon dark, missing all this. Doing "porridge" as they say,' McGinn said, staring over the terrace.

'Do you suppose they say "doing croissant" in French prisons?' Carolyn asked.

'Ah hae ma doots aboot tha'. I must say he had a nerve, walking into a supermarket, loading up a suitcase with bottles of champers and coolly walking out.'

'As the Cockneys say: "He had a lot of bottle".'

'But they've got a good case against him.'

'Stop, please. I might laugh and wake the neighbours.'

'No, that's strictly for the birds.'

'*Arrêt*,' said Carolyn. 'Come on - sleep. It's nearly five a.m.'

At midday they had an appointment with Fréderique and Patrice, but she was in a panic when they reached the café terrace.

'He's in jail,' she said, tearfully. 'The Sheriff arrested him and took him down to the Gendarmerie just before I got here.'

'Now calm down, Freddy. Sit down and have a drink. What exactly happened?' McGinn said.

'Armand, the café proprietor, saw it all. Just for a joke - to amuse me - Patrice did his eyes up with mascara so that he looked like a Chinaman: you know, almond-eyed.'

'That's not a crime.'

'No, but the point is the Sheriff didn't recognise him. He thought he was an escaped criminal or something. Patrice shouted: "But I'm Patrice, you idiot. We have a drink together almost every day," and then the Sheriff put the handcuffs on him and put him in the back of his van and drove him down to the Gendarmerie. He shouldn't have called him an idiot.'

'He was being kind to him,' McGinn said.

'He even produced his identity card - but of course the handsome young parachutist in the photograph bore no resemblance to the shaven-headed clown with mascara round his eyes who looked like

Mao-Tse-Tung's mother-in-law in drag.'

'Where's Patflic, the other cue-ball?' McGinn asked her.

'Gone fishing, where else? Don't they say you can never find a *flic* when you want one?'

Armand came out to the terrace: 'Freddy - stop worrying. I've been on the 'phone to the Brigadier and explained the mistake. He's coming up here with Patrice.'

A few minutes later a dishevelled Chinaman, the lardy-white of his pate now blemished with a touch of the sun and turning red, was delivered to the café by the Brigadier, a huge man with an expertly trimmed grey moustache, who shook hands with Armand and condescended to accept a soft drink as the day was now scorching hot.

'Your mascara's running,' said Frédérique to Patrice, who shamefacedly wiped the black goo off his eyelids.

McGinn saw the Brigadier looking at the girls. He removed his *képi*, took out a comb and gave a few deft flicks to his little iron-grey moustache while looking into his *képi,* held towards his face, wherein lay a tiny mirror.

'He's got a mirror in his hat,' McGinn said to Carolyn. 'I wonder if the Sheriff has a mirror in his hat?'

'No,' said Patrice, 'but he carries a piece of shit in his wallet.' He sipped his *pastis* and smiled. 'It's for identification purposes.'

When the Brigadier finished his orange juice and left, saluting, wishing everyone a *'bon journée'*, Armand came out and said: 'You'd better warn Jean-Paul that two men are looking for him, and from the look of them they want money or to take him to court for maintenance or both.'

'They'll never find him,' said Patrice. 'That cabin of his is pretty well hidden in the vines. I'll warn him, anyway. Thanks, Armand.'

'He'd better watch out,' said Frédérique. 'Hell hath no fury... etcetera. She's still annoyed about that file in the cake.'

'Not to mention the rope ladder and the ear-plugs, and that invitation to him from a certain *Rosbif* saying for a small fee he could have himself surgically deafened like the horses in the King's Troop that pull the guns in Hyde Park,' said Carolyn. 'No wonder poor Marie-Lise is annoyed.'

A battered banger screeched to a halt at the curbside.

Spider Smith leapt out.

'Can someone who speaks French and English come with me urgently to the *notaire's* office? I've been thrown out of my own house by bloody bailiffs who struck at dawn, and they've nailed up the front door, and my sodding Dutch tourists are due to arrive tomorrow. I had to kip in 'bis' when I got back from the *mechoui*. It's the old bat opposite. She's finally screwed me. I can't understand what they're rabbiting on about. I wasn't making any noise at all.'

Fréderique and McGinn sat on either side of Spider in the elegant office of the solicitor who had handled the sale of the property Spider had bought in his village.

'*Monsieur*,' McGinn started to say, but the solicitor snapped, '*Maitre*,' for McGinn had forgotten that French solicitors insist on this title to maintain their dignity. When a team of French grape pickers discovered that a cousin of Ginger's was a lawyer in England they spent the *vendange* calling 'bucket, if you please, *Maitre*,' and '*bon appetit, Maitre.*'

'You'd better handle this, Freddy,' McGinn said, and she asked the solicitor what the problem was. His French was so rapid McGinn lost track of the complications of the dispute between Spider and his neighbour, with much talk of *"vingt-trois and vingt-trois bis"*.

'It would appear,' said Fréderique, turning to Spider, 'that you have restored the wrong house.'

'The wrong house? What are you talking about?'

'The house you bought is twenty-three 'bis' and you, finding the front door of twenty-three swinging open, assumed that you had bought twenty-three and the ruin next door, twenty-three 'bis', whereas in actual fact, number twenty-three is owned by your neighbour opposite and she claims she told you a dozen times...'

'Bloody 'ell,' yelped Spider, jumping out of his seat. 'You mean I've spent fifteen hundred quid on restoring that old bag's house?'

'That is correct,' said Fréderique, a little smile lingering at the corners of her beautiful mouth.

'And I'm left with the shit-house next door?'

'Or the 'bis' house next door,' McGinn said.

'Shut up, you. It's not funny. Fifteen hundred bloody smackers down the karsi...'

'If Monsieur Smith,' said the solicitor, 'had been employing bonafide French workmen instead of a bunch of hairy, drunken English hippies working black and not paying taxes, it would have been explained to him.'

'She took her bleedin' time coming to you,' yelled Spider. 'She waited until I finished the work first...'

Fréderique translated for the solicitor who smiled blandly.

'My client suffers from arthritis,' he said.

'Arthritis,' Spider said with a snarl when Fréderique had translated for him. 'She doesn't suffer from arthritis - she has pyorrhoea, diarrhoea and gonorrhoea.'

'What does he say?' asked the solicitor.

'He says he's going to consult his legal advisers in England, Messrs Pyorrhoea, Diarrhoea and Gonorrhoea.'

'Very amusing, Mademoiselle, but my English is just good enough to understand his insults, and you can tell him that he has no chance of redress, no chance whatever of any contribution from my client towards his laughable jerry-building activities in the Rue de l'Eglise. Indeed, he has as much chance of getting money out of her - as I know to my own cost - as my arse has of shooting a peacock.'

They parted company with Spider back at the café where he dropped them, muttering under his breath certain threats not conducive to maintaining the *entente cordiale* or Anglo-French diplomatic relations.

Manouche had invited them out to see the beginnings of his construction of his snail farm, set in the rough woodland, where he was to make his fortune. The snail farm lay in a clearing, and there was a small wooden bungalow or pavilion which Manouche had acquired from the owner. It was rumoured that Manouche had borrowed a considerable sum of money from shop-owners, business people and bar owners in the vicinity, on the promise of massive returns for their investment in his venture. Manouche proudly showed the outlay, a series of green ceramic drain pipes, of ancient design, leading into little covered areas which had a sort of tin chimney for ventilation, and the breeding tunnels stretched all around the clearing.

'Is he nuts?' said Patrice when we left. 'There's no shade there. The one thing I know about snails is that they hate sun and love the dark. It must be hot in those pipes.'

'Humid, he claims,' McGinn said.

Peter Kinsley

'No-one breeds snails so near the coast,' said Patrice. 'It's too hot. There's a small factory near here but they get their snails from Eastern Europe.'

They went on to a picnic spot on the River Orb where it was possible to dive from a cliff face into water five metres deep, where Patrice was fishing with his family who had prepared a picnic of *brochettes* and salad, and Denis and Jo had organised a *pétanque* challenge, with a bottle of Ricard as the prize, which was won by Jean-Paul and shared out that evening.

The lazy holiday days drifted by.

It was time for a break, but Carolyn asked: 'What was in that letter you opened when we got back to the house yesterday?'

'Oh, it was very complicated, about the Bank de France but I was too tired to translate it all. We must be overdrawn.'

Waking up in their King-size bed next morning, McGinn threw the curtains back: 'Tra-la...' he announced as usual when the brilliant sunshine flooded in, lighting up the huge beams, the sunken living room, the far kitchen above the huge fireplace built by Jean-Paul, and the neat pointing by Pyrenees Tom, a regular grape harvester, of the stones laid at herringbone angles by Saracens around the year 700 added to stone cut by Roman slaves two thousand years ago.

'Today we are going to swim in two seas, and the day after tomorrow we'll sleep in Hemingway's room in Pamplona.'

'You're drunk,' said Carolyn.

'No. It's Happy Hour, the morning bonus from the night before, what the French call *"l'heure euphorique"*. I'll pack the tent.'

They had seen young Rupert off at Montpelier airport, a brave little boy of nine flying alone via New York to Miami to visit his Dad, Carolyn's first husband, re-married with two children, two cars, a house and a pool. Carolyn heard later from airline friends that most of the lady passengers and stewardesses who helped her well-behaved son to change flights in London and New York had wanted to adopt him. McGinn saw that he had inherited the charm of the old *boulevardier*, Rex, who had also made a hit with the ladies and was usually, like his twin Max, surrounded by them.

'Don't forget the casserole,' Carolyn called.

They had prepared a *boeuf bourguinon* ready for the weekend,

172

always taking one to Brusque, the trout fishing village in the Aveyron, an hour and fifteen minutes away, a magnificent village of cattle, meadows and fir trees in contrast to the vineyards of the Herault.

'We'll camp in Bayonne,' said McGinn, 'but first a swift dip in the Jolly old Mediterranean, the only sea, as Oscar Wilde said, fit for a gentleman to swim in - and ladies, too, of course. I can revert to form this evening in the Atlantic.'

A quick splash in Agde to start the heart, then on to Tarbes, a quick drink in a bar full of young paratroops doing their basic training, then on to Pau and the Atlantic coast, arriving in time to pitch the tent, have a swim in the cold Atlantic sea, dine on beef casserole and red wine, then a stroll through Bayonne to see the magnificent 14th of July fireworks display before the romance of sleeping in a tent by storm lantern near the sound of the Atlantic waves, as shadows danced on the canvas walls.

In Biarritz, the sea was choppy. Half a dozen back-packers huddled by the sea wall on a deserted beach, in their sleeping bags. It was time to move up into the hills, to St Jean-Pied-de-Port, crowded with tourists.

'Hemingway found some good places,' said Carolyn, 'and they're all popular now.'

'Yes, he travelled cheaply and lived economically. He was the forerunner: Paris, Schruns, the Basque country, working, ski-ing, fishing. The best things in life cost very little. Right - Roncevalles and Burguete across the Spanish frontier, then Pamplona...'

There was no breeze now, and with the 'enemy' overhead in Spain, the streets of Pamplona felt as if a great blanket had been spread over the town to entrap the summer heat and hasten Spaniards to their darkened bedrooms and *siesta*. Everything was closed for the afternoon, the streets deserted except for a few young soldiers on guard at military buildings, the occasional tourist, usually with Dutch number plates, stopping then driving on. There were very few French number plates. The French were avoiding the Basque country after a recent attack on all the French cars in a town after a demonstration by E.T.A when forty cars had their tyres slashed and the town hall paid for all the repairs. In Bayonne, some heroic E.T.A. freedom fighters had pulled the chromium *batons* off the sides of McGinn's car during the fireworks display celebrating Liberty, Equality, Fraternity...

'Come on, let's go,' Carolyn said. 'This town is dead.'

'No. It's sleeping - not dead. The Spanish siesta, and it's Sunday. It'll liven up this evening, just you wait and see.'

He asked a soldier and a policeman but they looked blank at his request for information about an hotel where an American writer had stayed in the 1920s and up to the outbreak of the Civil War in 1936.

The temperature rose and the heat bounced off the buildings.

'Come on, let's go,' Carolyn said again. 'It's nearly fifty years since Hemingway was here. You won't find it...'

'I once had to find a merchant seaman in Liverpool called Smith, and I found him... so...'

On the other side of the square, a few doors down, in what had once been the main street, an old man stood in a doorway. He wore a grey suit, a white shirt without a collar, and his clothes hung on him as if he had shrunk. His face was thin, cadaverous, cheeks sunken, a three-day growth of beard on his chin.

'*Perdon, Senor,*' McGinn said, '*soy un periodista Ingles. Donde es el hotel utilisar para el escritor American, Hemingway?*'

The old man interrupted him.

'He was my friend,' he said in English, and put his hand over his heart.

Eureka, thought McGinn - this was Montoya, as he was called in 'Fiesta', and the real name of the hotel was the Joldi, on the Avenue San Ignacio.

This was the hotelier who had organised all Hemingway's bullfight tickets, had introduced him to the top bullfighters of the day as an '*aficionado*'.

McGinn explained that he wanted to spend a night in the same room Mr Hemingway used. The old man said: 'My son will arrange it, but the rooms were divided up years ago, and are smaller now but it was the room I always gave him...' He looked sad, and put his hand to his heart again and said: 'He was my friend.' He appeared to be looking back into the past, his grey eyes watery. 'The old restaurant is no longer there, you know,' he said, coming out of his reverie. 'We changed it into a bar and snack bar - very American. Moving with the times, I suppose.'

The old man's son helped them in with luggage, and McGinn showed his French Government Press card and asked for a discount.

'*No problema, Senor,*' said the son, whose name was Marcos Darpa. 'I can give you a special discount on the out-of-season price.'

The room was small but very comfortable, with private bathroom. 'They probably made four rooms out of one,' he said, but Carolyn merely said: 'Sshhh... siesta time...'

At seven p.m. people began to sit at pavement cafés.

At seven thirty, as McGinn and Carolyn made their way to the famous bullring, they walked through narrow streets where all the little bars were filling up with teenage girls, in groups of three, four and five, snacking on *tapas*, sipping sherry and wine and coca cola, and talking animatedly.

'Emancipation,' said McGinn. 'Hard to believe that in 1973 in Ibiza all the girls were chaperoned and had to be in by 9 p.m. George's son, Steve, made a date and the girl turned up at the cinema with her father and two brothers...'

'Women's liberation finally came to Spain,' said Carolyn, joining the dark-eyed vivacious girls and ordering a Fina La Ina sherry for herself and a Bloody Mary for McGinn, after which he switched to red wine as they were given a small plate of food with each drink, pork *(lomo)*, meatballs *(albondigas)*, liver and onions and olives and cheese until McGinn said: 'No point in looking at menus in this town. We've had supper of *tapas.*'

Much, much later, in Hemingway's room, Carolyn said: 'I wonder if his bed was as comfortable as this? Why did you want to stay in Hemingway's room?'

'Have you ever noticed that there is a certain atmosphere, of peace, or pleasant euphoria, in the premises once inhabited by great artists? It is possible to sense it in Renoir's studio in Nice, or Van Gogh's little bedroom in Arles, or D.H. Lawrence's house in Vence, or even nearby, on a quiet evening in the garden of Keat's house where a nightingale often sings on a summer evening in that old mulberry tree. The numinous... beyond our understanding...'

'Haunted houses?'

'No. No ghostly figures, no shapes in human form, nothing earthbound, only a certain atmosphere, very peaceful, calming, as if a very special human being lived there, creating beauty all his or her life.

They never die, really. They continue to live in their works of art.'

'And the graves of writers?'

'Ah, that's just respect. Like H.L. Mencken visiting the grave of Edgar Allan Poe every Saturday night when he was drunk, and peeing on it. Or admiration, like the visitors to Edith Piaf and Oscar Wilde in Pere Lachaise or Karl Marx in Highgate, or Keats and Shelley in the English cemetery in Rome, but do you know the saddest graves I have ever seen? Those of the drummer boys, aged 12, in Gibraltar, after the Battle of Trafalgar.'

'Twelve?'

'England's cruelty to children. Gordon the Flute, who played in the town band in Ibiza was taken out of an orphanage at twelve and put in the Royal Navy and was aboard H.M.S. Ironside at the Spithead review in 1936... aren't you tired, Babba?'

'Yes. It's been a long day. A super day. A memorable day. Back home tomorrow...'

'Goodnight, Mrs B.'

'You know you are right, there is an atmosphere. I can actually feel your love for me here in this room...'

'Goodnight, sweet princess...'

'Goodnight, lover...'

'Goodnight, Ernesto...'

She chuckled: 'Goodnight, Mister Hemingway.'

'He was a much more sensitive man than the critics allowed, you know, and I think he feared the sensitive, feminine side to his macho nature, hence his homophobia. D.H. Lawrence had the same thing. What did Mailer call it? "A writer with the soul of a beautiful woman"...'

'Go to sleep.'

'Sorry.'

'You always want to talk at night.'

'Not another word... promissss...'

After a magnificent return drive, via Lourdes and Limoux, the panic began. Credit Lyonnais wanted every petrol cheque back from the garages en route, plus the 400 franc cheque from the veterinary surgeon who had amputated Midge's claw, otherwise the Bank de France would take away the cheque book for 12 months. Some kind of holiday fever had hit the computer operators in Lloyds Bank in England and they were claiming there were no funds, McGinn's 'account' having been mysteriously 'lost'. Having noted out of interest that petrol went up in price the further one drove from the Mediterranean landing ports, he had noted the names of the garages on the cheque stubs, sent money orders and retrieved the cheques - but the vet was on holiday, and the cheque was locked in his safe, and only he knew the combination. At 400 francs a claw, he was doing well and was holidaying in Thailand.

'So no cheque book for a year, and they claim no funds in England. Not to worry,' McGinn told Carolyn, 'I can borrow on the strength of doing the *vendange*, and then go back and sort it out.' He had learnt a short, sharp lesson about the ruthlessness of French banks about overdrawing.

'I'll borrow a thousand francs from Jean-Paul today,' he said.

'You'll be lucky,' said someone in the bar. 'He had a fire at his *cabanon* last night and it's burnt out. He's down there now raking through the ashes.'

'The only thing left is the grill,' said Jean-Paul sadly, looking at the charred wreck of his little home in the vines. 'It was the only that didn't burn.' He threw the well-used grill into the thick bushes.

'My money was in the mattress, unfortunately, and not down the well, where I should have put it. Trouble is I've no sense of smell. I'd left the gas open and couldn't smell it. As butane gas is heavier than air, it sinks into the well or lies on the ground. That's why yachts blow up, the gas sinks into the bilges. I lit a Gauloises, and BANG. I dived out. The heat and fire had risen to the ceiling. For a moment I thought I could get back in and get the money, but then the gas bottle blew up, and the roof collapsed.'

'Anybody got a tent I can borrow?' he said. 'There's a car coming,' said Carolyn.

'Quick - hide in the bushes,' said Jean-Paul. 'Where's your car?'

'Where I usually leave it, by the old barn on the main road. We walked up.'

Two men in city suits got out of a black Peugeot 304 and one of them consulted a piece of paper. 'Right at the Co-op cave, past four of Carignan, turn right at old barn, past three of Syrah, right at one of Carignan, reverse into Grenache, park, taking care to avoid deep ditch,' he read.

'This must be the place,' said the other.

'The usual instructions are: turn left at the railway station, right at the post office and left at the church. Here you need a track-reading scout to find places,' said the first official. 'But where's his cottage?'

'There's a heap of charred wood and bricks over there. That must have been it. We got here too late, it seems,' said his colleague.

'And a wife is hoping to get maintenance from this poor guy?' said the first, taking a document from his briefcase and scrutinising it.

'Well, the law is the law,' he added, taking the document over to what remained of the charred doorpost and pinning it securely to the black wood.

When they had gone, Jean-Paul pulled the document off the doorpost and read it, while the others looked over his shoulder.

'It's for *"prejudice moral"* and I have to pay a fine to the police and maintenance of a thousand francs a month plus back-payments. I'll bet those *justiciers* never had to pin a document like this on a piece of burnt wood before. I think they have to make a report and estimate the value of chattels and goods and property. I wonder what they'll write down? One sack of charcoal?'

'A good thing you hid that grill,' McGinn said.

'A good thing my nightingale wasn't singing in that tree. They might have taken that,' he chuckled.

Manouche was shouting on the café terrace where they adjourned with J-P to commiserate with his loss. 'I'll kill them. I'll kill them if I catch them,' he shouted.

Henry Catchpole sat on the terrace with a *demi* in his hand. 'It's Arsenic and Old Lace,' he said. 'They've released all his bloody snails into the woods. He's goin' potty, says the business is ruined. Cruelty to snails, they said. Kicked all the drain-pipes over. Caused a stampede, as Spider Smith said. But 'e won't find the old girls - they've gorn to Spain again, planning to attack a factory manufacturing fly-spray. Cruelty to flies, they say. Where will it end? They'll probably get an anti-aircraft gun and shoot down them planes that drop insecticide on the Camargue lakes every year. Cruelty to bleedin' mosquitoes. Or try and stop them bringing in them American vine roots. Cruelty to phylloxera insects.'

'You can't be serious about them going to Spain,' McGinn said to

Henry, who winked and whispered. 'They're still here, but don't tell Manouche. They're actually going to England tomorrow. You really started 'em orf when you told J-P abaht the 'orses in the King's Troop at Swiss Cottage being surgically deafened. I wish I'd never told 'em abaht it. Incensed is the word. '"Ow can 'er Majesty," Miss Elizabeth said, "'oo loves 'orses, allow this to 'appen?" "'Ow can 'er Royal 'Ighness, Princess Anne let it go on?" Miss Angela said, "The poor 'orses can't even 'arken to the 'ollerin' of the crahds or listen to the chirpin' of the birds in the park." They'll probably end up chainin' themselves to the bleedin' railings outside Buck 'ouse in protest and end up in the nick.'

'You could spray the area with a hosepipe, Manouche,' McGinn called to him, 'and the snails will think it's raining and you can get them all back again.'

'Ha! I could if there was a hosepipe. I could if there was *water*,' he said.

'You mean there's no water there?'

'Of course not. I have to carry it all. You don't get a piece of land like that cheaply if there's water on it. Water would make it valuable.'

'Don't wind 'im up any more,' said Henry Catchpole. ''e's in dead schtuck. 'is investors are making threats. They want their money back - quick. And 'is bird, the one that works in Geneva, came back on holiday to find a Dutch family living in 'er gaff. Manouche only sub-let it to Spider and they split the rent. She threatened to take 'im to court for not doin' 'er bathroom an' all that, as part of their contract, an' 'e said if she does 'e'll tell E.D.F. that she's fiddlin' on 'er meter.'

'How on earth do you know all this, Henry?' McGinn asked him.

'Radio Raymond. That's what they call 'im, cos 'e's got a mahf on 'im like the Mersey tunnel. Gets 'is info from that little turd in the *Mairie*. 'ot gossip. 'ot orf the press. Read all abaht it. Between you an' me and my four million readers...'

'I'll be glad when the *vendange* starts and everybody gets back to work,' McGinn said.

'You fixed up?'

'With Cristobal, the Spaniard. Carolyn, Ginger, Alfie, a couple of students from Paris, two American girls, also students, and Gilles driving the tractor.'

'Can you row me in?'

'I'll try. He's got one place for a bucketer.'

'That's for me. Tell 'im I'm definitely on.'

'What about the market?'

'Disaster story. Like your missus's shop. They look, they say *"Oo c'est mignone..."* but they don't buy anyfink.' He rolled an Old Holborn cigarette. 'The only fing they buy dahn 'ere,' he added, 'is food and booze.'

Not long before the *vendange* was due to start, parents started getting information about the schools starting again at the end of the first week in September.

Monsieur Berger delivered the papers from the *Mairie*, and McGinn asked him in for a drink, taking a bottle of his own grenache, the stuff that had laid out the workmen while building the house, and which McGinn had labelled with Monsieur Berger's name and the date of the wine.

'Nom de Dieu,' said M. Berger. 'That's marvellous wine. Where did you get that?'

McGinn took his hand away from the label and he laughed.

'I thought I had a competitor,' he said, chuckling.

'There's a question here,' said Carolyn when M. Berger had gone, '"How do you discipline your child?" What shall we say?'

'I don't know the French for thumb screws.'

'Be serious.'

'Put "mots". They'll like that, just words. It would be tempting to put something like, "English bread and water for three days with remission for good behaviour". We can scarcely tell them about the Camembert paper.'

Carolyn laughed. For a serious misdemeanour, like putting his finger on the top of the wine bottle and tipping more into his glass, he being allowed a thimbleful in his water-glass, Rupert got the Camembert paper under his nose so that with a shout of 'Ugh, no, help, not the Camembert paper,' he got a whiff that bore a close resemblance to the well-worn socks, grey, woollen of a Sergeant Major with trench foot. An over-ripe Saint-Mère was the most pungent.

During the next few days, the Spaniards started to arrive; later there would be train-loads of grape pickers, whole families of them from

Valencia and Alicante. A father and son working as porter and bucketer, the mother and two daughters working as cutters, then moving from the Herault to Bordeaux, and sometimes up to Switzerland for the later harvest, could make enough money to see them through the Spanish winter. They carried suitcases, but the cases did not contain suits: they were packed with tinned sardines and pâté, olive oil and garlic and coffee and powdered milk. They bought only bread in the French shops. A family of five were also paid 231 litres of wine over three weeks, the porter getting three litres a day and the others two litres. This they could sell back to the *patron* at a franc a litre.

The other foreigners were mainly English with some Irish, Dutch, a few Belgian and very few Germans. Reluctant to sell wine back to the *patron* at one franc a litre, the English and Irish, being unable to transport it back home in already overladen rucksacks, endeavoured to drink it. One Irish porter, Alfie, red hair gleaming, beard bristling, freckled face red with the sun, regularly drank his three litres each night to the accompaniment of a large repertoire of songs from his homeland. Most of his earnings went on the bars, treating everyone in sight with open-handed generosity, and he had been known to get his ticket back to Rotterdam from friends on the receiving end of his spending in order to get back to work labouring, or 'on the banjo' as he called it, meaning using a shovel.

Two young men came from Australia to meet up with pals from previous harvests. They worked in the desert as pipeline checkers, living in a bivouac. Because of the heat they worked at night in the bush, but as soon as the sun touched the horizon they ran and flung themselves into the tent, zipped it up, and stayed there throughout the day rather than be eaten alive by flies. To these highly-paid tough-guys, the back-breaking job of cutting grapes was a relaxing holiday.

Back-breaking it certainly was for the first three days and cutters would crawl painfully about the old barns where they were accommodated and collapse onto old army cots covered with straw palliases. On the fourth day of the twenty-one day harvest, the muscles and limbs got accustomed to the work, but by now it was the middle of September and that could bring rain and misery in the muddy fields. Tourists in warm cars will often shudder at the sight of a drenched and miserable team of harvesters in South West France in late September.

The *patron*, Cristobal, a huge, laughing, blond-haired Spaniard with a brightly coloured bandanna round his forehead and wearing a leather truss against back-ache from a lifetime stooping in the fields, sang arias and snatches from light operettas as the cutters worked. When he had called McGinn early to write the names of the grapes and the number allotted to him by the Co-operative to identify his tractor, McGinn realised that he was illiterate. With his French wife they had bought into the farm owned by an old lady of 80, the law allowing her to live her life out on the farm before the couple inherited it. During the *vendange* he broke off work to drive her to mass in the village and drive her back. Cristobal's only fault as a *patron* was his tendency to try to burn out overgrown ditches by the sides of his vineyards as the team worked. A scream from Carolyn or one of the American girls meant that he had almost set their shorts or blue jeans on fire as the flames leapt behind them and they jumped for safety. To make amends he gave them large bunches of magnificent flowers from his garden.

A team of local lads working the next vineyard called Carolyn over. 'They're showing off,' she said when she returned, 'they're eating raw snails. Just cracking the shells in their teeth and swallowing them.'

'Sure that's nothin',' said Alfie the Irish porter, 'I once saw a feller kill and eat a raw rabbit in a pub in Ireland. He did it just for the craic - and the five pound bet,' he added.

'I once saw a feller with a rat in a London pub,' said Henry Catchpole.

'STOP IT, please,' said Carolyn. 'That's enough horrible stories for one day.'

Cristobal kept glaring at the two Paris students. 'Hey, you two,' he yelled. 'You're eating more grapes than you pick. Stop eating and start working, will you?'

'We're trying to stop smoking,' one said.

Cristobal produced a pan which he heated over a small fire during the two-hour lunch break and offered everyone a taste of wild boar stew, which was delicious. He then curled up under an olive tree and slept for exactly one hour.

Next day he glared at the Paris students throughout the morning. 'He's annoyed,' one of the American girls said. 'They refused to read the *meteo* report on the TV screen last night because he called them lazy and said they ate too many of his grapes. The poor man can't read and write and we didn't know enough to tell him.'

'The students should have been on Georges Galette's two-day *vendange*,' said Ginger, rolling a cigarette. 'They'd have been so busy eating they wouldn't have thought of smoking. I thought I'd burst. A mountain of food you wouldn't believe: sausage, *pâté*, *rillettes*, olives, beetroot, celery, cucumber, chick peas, *ratatouille*, chicken casserole, pasta, salads, cheeses, cakes, you name it. In the afternoon, Madame came down to the vines with pizzas, *croque Monsieur*, *quiche Lorraine*. It was enough to burst Henry the Eighth.'

'Gee, you sure like French food, Ginger,' said one of the Americans. 'Do you like the people as much as their food?'

'Depends,' said Ginger. 'You know, I think all foreigners have a love-hate relationship with the French, and I think the French do with the British. Years ago I was hitch-hiking through France. In a street I went up to a house and asked for a glass of water. The house owner said: "If you're not out of this garden in two minutes, I'll call the police." A few doors further down the street I tried again. "Water?" the man said. "Don't you drink wine, you English? I hope you like roast chicken because you're invited to lunch with the family." That's what life is like: good and bad - everywhere.'

Ginger paused and looked back into the mists of time. His life was shared between grape harvest in Languedoc, and sojourns on a Kibbutz in Israel where he tried to lose the weight put on by his mother's cheese sandwiches in front of the television. Small adventures, like the one by canoe from England to Agde (he sold the canoe for 100 Francs upon arrival) were put aside for a University course to prepare him for life in Swaziland, finding water for the natives, and turning down a farmer's offer of his 15-year-old daughter in exchange for a cow.

'Sometimes, of course, you think these viticulteurs are being kind when they're not, and having an ulterior motive. Working for a *patron* in Gabian, his wife asked me where I went between 12 and 2 p.m. I told her the bar, where I ate my sandwich, prepared that morning, and had a couple of beers. She told me not to go to the bar next day but to come to the family house at midday. I was flattered, a foreigner being invited to eat *en famille* with a grape farmer and his wife, and indeed there was a lavish meal where ten of the family sat around the table: soup, pâté, salad, chicken and vegetables, when I arrived next day.

Then the wife said: "Where's your sandwich?"

It was her ploy to stop me having those two beers, so that I would not be sleepy and would work harder in the afternoons. I had a bit of bread and cheese in the kitchen.

'A few days after the *vendange* was over, I discovered that the husbands could be as tight as the wives. I bought the patron a beer in the bar and he said to me: "Would you like a drink?" When I said I would he took me in his car to the family cave and sloshed out a dirty glass, poured red wine from a cask and gave it to me.'

'I think, like me, you're still a bit naive, Ginge - you expect people to behave well and they just don't. I once put up the idea for a film on the Battle of Waterloo long before others had thought of it and invited my old school friend to script it with me. I took him to meet the producer, Norman Miller, and we met the Colonel of the Guards who agreed to supply the men. Then I heard nothing, and assumed Miller had been unable to get finance for it. Then I met my old school pal and was invited with Carolyn to dinner. I expressed my sorrow at the untimely death of Miller, killed on an autobahn in his Mini, and my old buddy pal said: "Yes, and Coutts Bank wouldn't cash the cheque he had given me." I stood up and said it's time to leave, and he saw that he had put his foot in it. I felt sick. I'd known him for 25 years.'

'Seems like they both got their come-uppance for robbing you, said Ginger. 'Did you do anything about it?'

'Yes. I didn't speak to him ever again...'

'STOP THE TALKING' shouted the *patron*.

'Oops,' said Ginger, 'I got sacked at Cabriere two years ago for making roll-ups during working hours.'

'They get their money's worth, these farmers,' said McGinn. 'Yet they'd rather lose a harvest than cut the lunch break down to one hour, and they'll waste an hour with the whole team looking for a pair of 3-francs *secateurs*, and they always wait until everyone is soaked to the skin before they call a halt for rain and take shelter.'

When the aches and pains disappeared after the first week, instead of flopping out on a bed or sinking into a bath, McGinn and Carolyn visited bars in other villages. From Alignan-du-Vent came the reverberating rhythm of Spanish guitars heard from miles away on the still, night air. Some families had brought young children and they danced flamenco to the guitar accompaniment, stamping little feet and clapping hands and clicking castanets. In other villages, in other bars, the sound of Scottish and Irish folk songs and English pop music filled the air. The floors awash with beer and wine, singers hung by their fingers to the corbels of brass-railed bars and tried to drown each other out. Outside in doorways and alleyways, furtive joints of marijuana were smoked in secret. Around and around a crystal clear pool beneath a war memorial, an Irishman, stark naked, swam in circles, scattering goldfish while his pal Alfie shouted from the public bench: 'Do you want the shampoo, Noël?'

Jean-Paul paid for everyone with a five hundred franc note and Henry Catchpole strummed the notes of 'Blueberry Hill' on his guitar.

The final paying-out day at the end of the harvest was done with great formality, the whole family present in the living room while the *patron* called each porter or bucketer or cutter and pay was handed out, then wine was served and cakes eaten with great ceremony and handshakes all round. A couple from a nearby farm did the paying-out for Cristobal, writing down each amount while the *patron* shook hands with each recipient of the twenty-one days' wages.

Over the next few days the *vendangeurs* left for their various destinations, the packed trains to Valencia and Alicante; teams on the road to Bordeaux; patched and painted camper vans heading for Spain to await the orange-picking season in November and December. Other camper vans were heading for Greece and the tail end of the olive harvest and later the orange picking.

The American girls were making for Rome, via Florence and Venice; Henry Catchpole was taking his new fiancée, Corinne, to London to meet his Mum; Ginger was off to Israel, to his Kibbutz, Hagosharim, for the tail end of the apple and cotton harvest, where Uzi machine guns were issued to the men at night as they had been to McGinn and others in case of attack across the border on the Golan Heights. Alfie's girl-friend, Marion, was joining him for a holiday in Spain. Gilles was returning to Brittany, to set up market stalls with his friend Yvon, who had a degree in Chinese from the Sorbonne, making them the best educated barrow-boys in France, if not in Europe. The Paris students said they had stopped smoking, but had learnt to drink more. Spider Smith, having earned exactly the amount of his bar bill, cheerfully paid up, had a baby whisky on the house and set off hitch-hiking north, his old banger resting in the scrapyard after another and fatal confrontation with the church in his village. Ben Aissa and his Moroccan friend took the bus from Beziers down through Spain to Malaga to catch the boat home where they would stay four months with their wives and families. Siddo was bottling apple purée and making nut wine; Pierre was playing Tombola and trying to win a turkey or a mountain ham in the local bars.

Manouche was a wanted man.

What had remained of his snail farm in the woods had been blown sky high by one of his creditors, possibly by lighting a candle and opening the gas bottle. Once the cochineal insect had fed on the surrounding 12-foot high Kermes oaks, gathered for its dye, but now the trees known as the *'maquis'* good for hiding in, were decorated with the carcasses of many snails and a pair of Manouche's underpants and one sock.

'I wonder if we will ever see him again,' said Carolyn as they sat on the terrace.

'Or any of them.'

'They come and go.'

'Tom Plumb is still here. We're building a swimming pool for a judge, and the judge invites us to lunch every day in the chateau with his whole family. The judge's wife serves me, Tom Plumb and Henry Catchpole tea on the lawn at 8.30 a.m.'

'Liberté, égalité, fraternité,' said Carolyn.

'Yes. Somehow I cannot imagine an English judge doing that. Bash is still on the building site. Dave went home to the Aude.'

'Poor Manouche. I hope he comes back some day.'

'Well, wherever he is, he's teaching some boys to fish or how to find mushrooms or how to snare a rabbit or catch frogs by moonlight, with great new ideas of making a fortune in import-export or something like that. He may be back some day. We'll give a party for him.'

'Yes, a *mechoui*.'

'They come and go, as you say,' Peter McGinn said, looking down towards the valley of the butterflies below the village. 'Just like butterflies, here today and gone tomorrow, like the Mayfly, the ephemera that trout love. Don't worry, they'll be back next year, the old magnet will draw them back.'

'Imagine coming all the way from Australia.'

'It must be good here.'

'It's a drag, having to go back to London. Bloody banks.'

They said farewell on the station platform as the Paris train pulled in, on time as always. A kiss, a shout of *au revoir*, one last look at her amaranthine beauty and off, charging through the night.

In the corridor outside McGinn's compartment, two English girls with rucksacks were arguing with the ticket inspector. 'Do you speak French?' one of them asked plaintively. 'We can't follow what he's saying. We've got tickets but he...' The little moustachioed martinet with the stars on his cap said: 'Tell them this is a sleeping-compartment-only train. They must buy *couchettes*.'

'Oh, we have to pay for beds, but they're expensive,' said one of the girls when McGinn had translated. 'We'll have to think about that. We're on a tight budget.'

'What do they say?' asked the inspector.

'They say they're thinking about it,' McGinn replied.

'Tell them to think quickly,' he snapped. 'They're in France now. If they don't pay, I'll put them off at the next station.'

The girls reluctantly opened their purses...

The boat train from Paris to Calais was unusually full, with excursion passengers occupying every seat in the compartments and the expensive dining car. McGinn had a tin of sardines, half a *baguette* and a tomato, but where to eat the sandwich? He could scarcely spill sardine oil on the well-dressed passengers. McGinn, experienced economy-class traveller, knew a private place...

In the washroom, he was about to take the first bite when a call, *'Billets s'il vous plait'* accompanied a loud banging on the door.

'Occupé,' he called out.

Suddenly a key turned in the lock, the door was flung open and there stood another star-spangled manikin. He looked at McGinn. McGinn, open-mouthed, looked at him. He looked at the sandwich.

'Vôtre billet, s'il vous plâit,' he said, and punched the ticket, saluted, and as he left he called over his shoulder: *'Bon appetit, Monsieur.'*

He had to laugh, and admit that Ginger had been so right about the good and bad and the love-hate relationships between the nationalities, and end up liking the French in their own, clever , individualistic way.

Where else would they wish a good appetite to a penurious traveller snatching a bite in the loo? Where else would a judge eat with a plumber and have his wife serve him tea? Where else would a lorry driver with vines serve a meal fit for a king to his grape pickers? Where else in a first class restaurant would they serve with courtesy and respect a plasterer in splattered bedroom slippers? Where else could one shoot over other men's land without getting or asking permission? Where else does a litre of excellent wine cost the same as two postage stamps? Where else would you see a policeman kissing his son on both cheeks while on traffic duty? Where else would a farmer's wife say, as Siddo once said: 'All the great artists died in poverty.' Or a bar where a garage mechanic said: 'So you are a writer, Monsieur? Welcome to Pézenas. There hasn't been a writer here since Molière died.'

The wine growers of the Languedoc are simple men whose lives are lived to a rigid routine, as rigid as the eight-hour day, the two-hour lunch, the monotonous pruning of the vines, and everything in season and according to the cycle of nature, a time to fish and a time to mend the nets, a time to grow and a time to harvest, a partridge eating the farmer's grapes, then the farmer eating the partridge for his dinner.

With the white cliffs of Dover in sight, the words of William Morris came to mind: 'Wealth is what nature gives us and what a reasonable man can make out of the gifts of nature... the sunlight, the fresh air, the unspoilt face of the earth, food, raiment and housing necessary and decent, the storing up of knowledge... the power of disseminating it... works of art, the beauty which man creates when he is most a man, most aspiring and thoughtful... *that is wealth.*'

The bank clerks gave the computer a kick or whatever they do to correct or cover up their errors and with a quick reverse kneecaps the return journey began. The best part of the night train journey from Paris is the early morning with the sun on the red tiled roofs of the houses and the game of 'spot the first olive tree' can be played. After the first olive tree, the south begins, and with the French law insisting that all roofs in this region are made of red tile, the panorama of the towns and villages is magnificent when lit up by the early morning sun.

The vines were a riot of Autumnal colours, whole vineyards dark red or bright yellow or russet, and the vines that were trained up the sides of houses were now bright red, making the houses seem aflame. Schoolchildren were on the bus, vivacious brown-eyed girls and solemn boys reading and glancing out of the window at the oyster and mussel beds of the Bassin de Thau and the shimmering Mediterranean beyond the lake. Stallholders were putting lemons amongst the mussels and oysters to add colour to the display. The newsagent-tobacconists and the bread shops were busiest at this time in the morning, but the autumn fruit, the melons, pears, plums, apples, were already on display outside the grocers' shops.

The streets of Pézenas were silent, the Place Gambetta deserted, the ancient stones still in shade. Across this square had walked Queen Anne of Austria and Cardinal Mazarin before the enthronement of the young Louis XIV. Was that the ghost of D'Artagnan lurking in the shadows? Was that Porthos with him, the pair of them now secret agents for Mazarin? Were Athos and Aramis behind that pillar?

Men were out with guns now, and bird dogs quartered the vines to flush quail and partridge, rabbit and pheasant, into range, and bright green blue red and yellow 12-gauge shells lay amongst the rotting *sarments* of yesteryear in the fields now stripped of fruit.

From the huge Co-operatives came the aroma of wine, seeming to steep into the stones and trees of the villages, filling the air with the heady scent of the harvest. Families were out gathering mushrooms in pine woods or beneath the scattered leaves, brittle and holly-like, of the Kermes oak, seeking *chanterelles* and *cèpes* and *bolet* or the white field mushrooms on terrains where horses had been kept, or the *langue de boeuf* which looks like a bull's tongue protruding from a tree stump, and all the edible fungus that grows out of wood.

The *vendangeurs'* peach tree outside the house was already shedding a few leaves. When it had been shaken, the fruit had rolled down the little hill towards the stream, with Carolyn running after them to gather them.

Beyond the hill opposite the terrace was the *maquis* where the wild boar hid, and below that a hillock covered with *genet*, the roots of the broom almost impossible to remove, its name taken by the Plantagenet kings of England to confirm their permanence: *planta genet*.

In the valley of the butterflies, all was silent. The only sign of the wild boar was the spoor in the soft yellow clay of the footpath, for the sound of guns had sent them into hiding in the deep, impenetrable scrub. The bark of guns far away in the distant hills indicated where men in green surrounded a thick forest and waited all day while beaters, small wiry men, ran behind the hunting dogs through the low tunnels made by the *sangliers*, trying to flush the prey into the open.

A charging, wounded boar could mean death or severe injury to a hunter. Built for fighting and running, their sharp tusks can rip open an adversary with a swift uplift of the head. The hunters were thinning out the herds before the rutting season in December and January when the normally reclusive and solitary males joined the herd, and later the sows produced litters of a dozen young, the striped *marcasin* being able to forage for themselves after a fortnight. The hunters usually return empty-handed, or spend a lot of time retrieving their valuable dogs from the thickets where only the boar, with its thick skin and bristles and underhair can penetrate, the dog's bell on its collar guiding the beater to its rescue.

The two sounds that permeate the still air of the Languedoc from the start of *'la chasse'*, the hunting season, until Mardi Gras are gunfire and the sawing and chopping of wood for the fires. The short winter was usually mild, but there was a snowfall every ten years or so, and lemon trees, geraniums and certain cactus had to be protected with straw against frost which could kill off bougainvillaea or other sub-tropical plants.

In the villages and towns, the people settled back into early evenings and tombola in the cafés, and television, which was the winter routine. By eight in the evening the streets were deserted and dark and windswept. It was time to follow the sun.

Midge the cat was given a tranquilliser and put in the wickerwork cat basket. Wine and cheese as gifts for friends in Spain were packed and put in the car, and the house was locked until the Spring.

The land was asleep for four months and the grape pickers scattered to the four winds, but many of them would be back when the grapes were ripe and ready for harvesting. They would come from the industrial cities of the north, from Paris and Rotterdam, from Ireland and England and Germany, from Spain, from America and Australia, and soon from Eastern Europe, for the grapes that make the best wine must be picked by hand, and the quality of Herault wine was improving each year.

They would return as the butterflies return each year to the valley, for a brief, bright, sunny time. Some would be caught by the swifts and the swallows that swooped endlessly in flight over the valley; some would dash themselves against trees and have broken wings; the rest would mate and sunder, and the eggs would become caterpillars, and the caterpillars would become chrysalis and spin cocoons, and when the weather was warm again the chrysalis would emerge and grow wings and take off on a flight through the valley of the butterflies.

Also published in 2002

Memoirs

Volume III

Bogged Down
in
County Lyric

Under sail with Tristan Jones in Ibiza

Peter Kinsley

see over...

Volume III

The author on his travels meets characters in London (Hampstead, Fleet Street, Soho), New York (The Chelsea Hotel, Greenwich Village), Minneapolis, Mexico (Acapulco, Zihuatanejo), Greece (Corfu, Paros), Turkey (Istanbul), Israel (Jerusalem, Haifa, Hagosharim Kibbutz), Italy, France, Germany, and on the island of Ibiza, where he introduces the reader to a hundred characters with fifteen nationalities as Ibiza began to get famous.

* * *

"In New York, the Irish-American nurse, having ascertained that he was a Welshman, said that the British Army was getting a bad beating in the Falklands war, and added that his fellow countryman, Dylan Thomas had died in the very bed he was in at that moment.

Tristan Jones said: 'Oh yes, and have you any other good news?'

'Yeah, we took your leg off last night,' she replied with menopausal charm.

It was some years later, in Thailand, that his other leg was amputated, and he discarded his whalebone false leg for a little motor-scooter."

* * *

A New York publisher was about to bring out my first novel, a comedy set in London about a young con-man who lived inside the big blue whale in the Kensington Natural History museum to avoid paying rent, and they had booked me into the Chelsea Hotel, home of Arthur Miller, Tennessee Williams, Arthur C. Clarke, Jack Kerouac, Allen Ginsberg, Tom Wolfe, Brendan Behan, and Dylan Thomas in his day.

And that is where my story opens.

Absenta Friends

Two of the many characters
of Ibiza.

Madrilas, below with kitten,
who drank the George and
Dragon dry as he painted it
black and white (see p. 317
of Volume III), and Russian
George, actually Estonian,
a tourist guide who quit on
hearing one American
matron ask another on his
bus near Marrakesch:
'Is that the same moon we
see at night in Texas?'

Photos: Axel Blazejczak

195